CONGENITAL ANOMALIES OF THE VISCERA

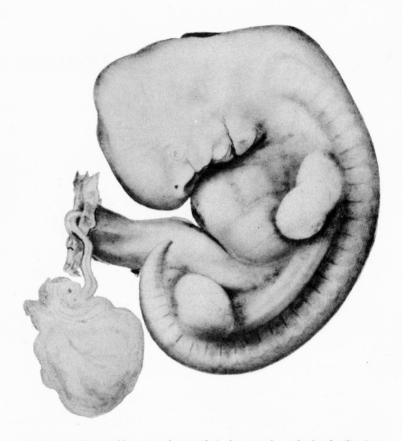

Fig. 1. Lateral view of human embryo early in the seventh week after fertilization.

CONGENITAL ANOMALIES OF THE VISCERA

Their Embryological Basis

J. LEWIS BREMER, M.D.

*Hersey Professor of Anatomy, Emeritus,
Harvard University, and The Children's Hospital, Boston*

HARVARD UNIVERSITY PRESS · CAMBRIDGE

1957 ——

ⓒ Copyright 1957 by the President and Fellows of Harvard College

Distributed in Great Britain by Oxford University Press, London

Library of Congress Catalog Card Number 56-13344

Designed by Burton J. Jones, Jr.

Photocomposition by Graphic Services, Inc., York, Pennsylvania

Printed in the United States of America
by The Murray Printing Co., Wakefield, Massachusetts

Bound by Stanhope Bindery, Inc., Boston, Massachusetts

PREFACE

The courses in embryology commonly required for the medical degree stress especially the early stages of normal development, from the fertilization of the ovum to the origin and primary growth of the various organs and systems, and of the body as a whole. A working knowledge of these subjects is essential to the understanding of this present book. In these courses the accent is chiefly on the normal; in only a few textbooks on the subject are abnormal conditions considered. For the graduate in medicine who is starting an internship or residency in pediatrics, and for one already engaged in the practice of this branch of medicine, these courses leave much to be desired. Confronted by the various types of congenital malformations so often exhibited by the young patients, he feels strongly the need of further knowledge of the later fetal or prenatal or even postnatal growth, and of the abnormal possibilities as well as the normal sequences of developmental processes. To supply this need, at least in part, and to call attention to the delicate adjustments, both in time and in the relative positions of the various parts, by which normal development is achieved and without which anomalies are certain to occur, this book has been written.

Almost all of the known forms of recognized abnormalities in the various organs can be traced to some simple disturbances of the growth sequence. As expressed by Shaner, *Anat. Rec. 118*, 539–560 (1954), in writing of the heart, "In general, a simple arrest of development, followed by a halting resumption of growth, complicated by hydrodynamic forces and other minor but well known disorders, will explain the most complicated heart abnormalities." In other cases, the growth of a part may be accelerated instead of arrested, or the change of growth rate may be located at an unusual position, and these changes may result in an entirely different type of

v

anomaly. The ultimate cause of these slight local changes of growth rate may be chemical or hormonal or thermal, the first two being transmitted to the embryo from some deficiency in the maternal diet [for example, J. Warkany, *Vitamins and Hormones 3*, 73–103 (1945); C. D. C. Baird, M. M. Nelson, I. W. Monte, and H. M. Evans, *Circulation Res. 2*, 544–564 (1954)], the thermal caused by intercurrent acute maternal disease. Chronic or heritable maternal disease seems to be commonly reflected in a general debility of the ovum, rendering it unduly sensitive to adverse conditions, although cases showing the definite inheritance of specific abnormalities have been recorded; but the belief that systemic and multiple malformations are always due to heredity through changes in the germ-plasm is of doubtful validity. Whatever the inciting cause of the changes in growth rate, it is efficient for an organ only if active at a certain critical period of the initiation of that organ's development, in the early period of pregnancy. The resultant sequences leading to the development of the anomaly can usually be readily followed. From the knowledge of these developmental sequences new types of abnormality, either hitherto undescribed or published merely as rare and unexplained findings, can be understood and traced to their embryological sources. No attempt has been made to collect all or even the major part of these rare or new anomalies, but the number of them found in a large children's hospital is surprising.

Certain malformations of the central nervous system have been mentioned only as connected with or resulting from an anomaly of some other organ. The brain and spinal cord are too vast and too intricate a subject to be properly considered here.

To complete the story for each organ or system, the normal development is rapidly reviewed, and as aids for this review many of the simple drawings by Professor F. T. Lewis, which have served well in his and my former textbooks of histology, have been retained here. Others are from former papers of mine, and for many of these, as well as for several new drawings prepared for this book, I am glad to thank Miss E. Piotti, whose skill is already well known. Many other illustrations have been taken from these and from other published sources. For permission to use this material I am sincerely grateful. Also, I wish to acknowledge with many thanks the constant help and encouragement offered by my colleagues in this

PREFACE

hospital, Drs. W. E. Ladd, T. W. Lanman, E. B. D. Neuhauser, R. E. Gross, J. Craig, and many others who, by supplying many illustrations for my use and much-needed advice for the text, have made this book possible. Finally, special thanks are due to Dr. Sidney Farber, for his great kindness in reading the manuscript for me and for his many helpful suggestions.

J. L. BREMER

CONTENTS

1 ———

THE RESPIRATORY
AND ALIMENTARY SYSTEMS
Nose, Mouth, and Face

The entrances both to the respiratory and to the alimentary systems form portions of the face.

The early embryo, during the differentiation of the germ layers, consists of a flattened sheet forming the common wall of the yolk sac and the amniotic cavity. The upper or dorsal layer of this sheet is of ectoderm continuous with the lining of the amnion; the bottom or ventral layer is a continuation of the yolk sac entoderm. On this flat disk a central darker spot, the primitive knot or Hensen's node, represents the rapid local multiplication of cells, and a less prominent lineal extension of the node, called the primitive streak, marks the future caudal end of the embryo. Cranially from the node extends the notochord, between the surface ectoderm and the underlying entoderm, and dorsal to the notochord the ectoderm thickens as the paired parallel medullary or neural plates, which are to form the spinal cord and brain. The plates and the notochord grow forward rapidly and soon dominate the diminishing primitive streak and node, until the latter appears as a minute terminal structure at the caudal end of the spinal cord. The neural plates soon outdistance the notochord in forward growth, and, once beyond it, their cranial tips bend abruptly ventrally, perhaps to conserve linear space.

The face of the embryo begins to take form after the completion of the first or head bend of the projecting head fold, as a result of which the forebrain region lies at right angles to the rest of the body. The foregut has grown forward from the yolk sac to meet a shallow surface depression, the stomodaeum, at the still intact oral plate or oral membrane, composed of the fused surface ectoderm and foregut entoderm. Along the sides of the head are developing three pairs of sense organs (or integral parts of sense organs), the paired olfactory and otic organs and the lens for each eye. They first appear as rounded or oval areas of thickened surface ectoderm, called placodes, which, as development proceeds, sink into the underlying mesenchyma as depressed cups or pits open to the surface. In this condition the olfactory organs remain permanently; the placodes for lens and for inner ear sink deeper, lose connection with the surface epithelium, and remain as closed vesicles surrounded by mesenchyma, awaiting further differentiation (Fig. 2). In many ways this development resembles that of the central nervous system, in that the latter also is initiated by the formation along the back of the embryo of two parallel linear thickenings of surface ectoderm, the neural plates, which then become depressed as the neural groove, close over as the neural tube, and sink below the surface.

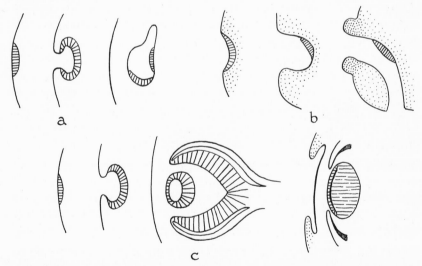

Fig. 2. Diagrams to show placodes and development of (a) ear, (b) nose, and (c) lens.

The first placodes to appear, in point of time, are those for the inner ears. At 19 days, in the seven-somite embryo, the otic placodes can be detected as rounded areas of thickened ectoderm, one on each side of the head over the hindbrain. Soon they pass through the open-cup stage to become closed vesicles, the otocysts (Fig. 2, *a*), which later differentiate into the epithelial cochlea, the semicircular canals, and the entire ectodermal inner ear. Each otocyst sinks deep in the surrounding tissues and between it and its parent skin ectoderm develops the first or most anterior of a series of branchial pouches from the pharynx and corresponding branchial clefts or grooves on the side of the head, to be described in the next chapter. Each cleft runs from over the otocyst ventrally toward its fellow of the opposite side, and may be considered as the boundary line between face and neck. The otic placodes themselves are important at present only as a guide to the position of the clefts. The first clefts are important landmarks in face development.

The olfactory placodes are situated in the skin ectoderm at the morphologically cranial end of the head, ventrolateral to the forebrain. Appearing during the fourth week, they soon form deep open depressions, the olfactory pits, but, instead of closing off as vesicles, these pits remain open, grow deeper, curve, and finally open to the surface again at a point that is later to be included within the mouth (Fig. 2, *b*). The pits actually form the nasal passages, within which a small area only is modified as the olfactory organ.[1] Also, on the median wall of each nasal passage an additional minor pit develops to lodge the vomeronasal, or Jacobson's organ. This is apparently an independent sense organ, possibly for underwater olfaction in lower forms.[2] In man it remains vestigial. Around the opening of each olfactory pit a broad raised rim develops, incomplete on the lower side (Fig. 1, frontispiece), where a groove is directed morphologically ventrally toward the stomodaeum.

The lens placodes appear, at about 5 weeks, at the sides of the head, also over the forebrain, but caudal to the olfactory pits, and pass through the open-cup stage to become sunken vesicles (Fig. 2, *c*). In certain of the molluscs (e.g., Limax, a naked snail) vision is received by the placode itself; the cells of the deep layer of the vesicle elongate as visual receptors and transmit the visual sensation to dendrites of nerve cells in the proper sensory ganglion. A chitinous lens is provided by the overlying surface ectoderm. In the vertebrates, as acute vision becomes more important for active life, the placode eye is reduced to a subsidiary role, acting merely as a much more plastic optic lens, while the sensory visual receptors are transferred to the retinal layer of the *optic vesicle,* a structure that by its origin as a hollow outgrowth from the outer edge of the alar plate of the still open forebrain (i.e., the most cranial portion of the neural crest), by its distinctive pattern of growth close to the side of the brain in a morphologically ventral direction, and by its terminal expansion and slender connection with the parent brain, can be likened to a sensory ganglion and considered as the most cranial member of the long line of dorsal root ganglia, which also show primarily a slight cleftlike cavity.[3] The optic vesicle expands dorsally, close to the side of the brain, and then is indented to form the two-layered optic cup, the inner layer of which serves as the retina. Yet, although they no longer are to serve as visual receptors, the cells of the deeper wall of the lens vesicle still elongate and to such an extent that they soon fill the vesicular cavity and transform the lens vesicle into a solid body, which is taken into the open mouth of the optic cup and there permanently attached. The eye is thus formed by the combination of two entities, the brain wall and the overlying skin ectoderm each supplying a share. Together they produce on the side of the head a rounded mound surrounded by a curving groove which continues as a straight open furrow or sulcus to the ventral surface of the head and there opens into the stomodaeum in common with the groove from the nasal placode (Fig. 3, *a*).

In the later development of the eye, at about 7 weeks, the protruding mound of the eyeball and its surrounding groove are progressively buried by the growth of two folds of ectoderm and supporting mesoderm, derived from the outer rim of the circular groove. These are the eyelids, and they are oriented in the face as definitely upper and lower, without regard to the orientation of the retina or of the eyeball itself. For the greater part of fetal life the lids are shut and fused, enclosing the conjunctival sac, from the lateral angle of which the lacrimal glands grow out as a group of primarily solid epithelial buds. From near the medial angle two other epithelial buds grow out and soon join as a single rod, which then lengthens and joins the adjacent nasal cavity as the forerunner

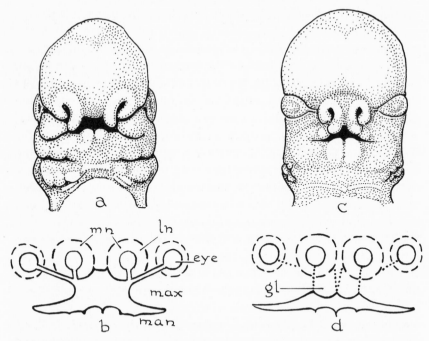

Fig. 3. Frontal aspect of faces of human embryos of (a) 9 mm and (c) 12 mm (after Patten); (b, d), diagrams to show relation of face to nasal and lens placodes and to mouth; *lm, mn,* lateral and mesial nasal processes; *max, man,* maxillary and mandibular processes; *gl,* globular process.

of the nasolacrimal duct,[4] later canalized. Other authors [5, 6] derive this duct from the deeper cells of the open furrow from the eyeball, reoriented in a slightly different direction and joining the two outgrowths from the inner canthus at one end and the nasal cavity at the other. The original groove from eyeball to stomodaeum is ultimately closed.

In relation with each placode, then, there is at one time a ventrally directed groove. Still another pair of lateral head grooves develops as the result of the head bend, which causes a crease around the ventral surface of the head in the region of the midbrain, continued for a certain distance on the lateral surfaces. Each lateral crease is provided with a branch running caudally, and these paired branches determine the location of the future mouth. With the continued rapid forward growth of the brain and the retarded growth of the ventral part of the head, these branches are carried to a relatively more caudal position between the eyes and the first branchial clefts.

The four grooves at the side of the head—nose, eye, mouth, ear —divide this region into four "processes." Beginning at the morphological tip of the head, the first of these are the median and lateral nasal processes (I and II), separated by the nares and nasal grooves; the lateral nasal process is limited by the optic groove, and thus includes both the raised rim of the nasal passage and the flat surface between that and the groove running ventrally from the eyeball. Between the optic groove and the mouth is the maxillary process (III), and between the mouth and the first branchial cleft lies the mandibular process (IV). At the front of the head, between the upper parts of the two median nasal processes, is the unpaired median nasal field or frontonasal process. Because of the head bend the nasal processes point in a direction at right angles to the maxillary and mandibular processes; by their future growth and union the various processes form the face.

Formation of the face. The two median nasal processes grow downward and fuse with each other below and with the median nasal field above (Fig. 3). The tip of each process, below the external naris, becomes rounded and is known as the processus globularis. The lateral nasal processes, on the other hand, remain short and allow the maxillary processes, finding vacant space below them, to grow across their lower ends and meet the sides of the globular processes, thereby closing the optic and olfactory grooves and shutting out the lateral nasal processes from any participation in the upper lips. The mandibular processes, longest of them all, meet in the midline, and by themselves form the whole of the lower jaw. Each fuses superficially along the side, for a varying distance, with the maxillary process to make the cheek; the extent of this fusion determines the size of the mouth, too long a fusion causing an abnormally small mouth, microstomia, too little fusion resulting in macrostomia. In the latter case the red of the lips may be of normal proportions, not reaching to the border of the opening.

The protruding nose develops during the fourth month by the forward growth of a single cartilaginous septum, derived from the unpaired nasal field, and of several paired median and alar cartilages, derived from the median and lateral nasal processes. The paired nature of the tip of the nose can always be felt and often seen. The globular processes do not contribute to this late growth, but remain at the former level to serve as the lips. The external nares, which at 2 months still remain in the plane of the face, are turned down to a more horizontal position by this late growth of the cartilaginous septum. The new space thus formed is the vestibulum nasi. The attachment of the alae nasi to the face shows that only the rim around the olfactory pit is concerned in this growth, in other words, that the lateral nasal process extending laterally to the optic groove is actually divisible into the rim portion and a flat portion, and that these two portions may act individually. This fact will help to explain the relations seen in certain anomalies.

The palate. Within the mouth, from the oral surface of each globular process and of the anterior half of each maxillary process, a shelflike projection grows inward toward its fellow from the opposite side. These are called respectively the median, or premaxillary, and the lateral palate processes. It will be remembered that the nasal pits open posteriorly into the top of the oral cavity. The continued growth and final fusion of the palate processes from all four sources (the incisive foramen marks the extent of the premaxillary contribution) form the permanent palate, shutting off the upper part of the oral cavity. The various forms of cleft palate can be recognized as being due to the failure of certain elements to attain their normal growth. The nasal septum joins the palate from above. These several fusions serve to extend the nasal passages at the expense of the upper part of the oral cavity, and to move the choanae to the posterior end of the hard palate. Below the palate shelves a deep groove, the labial fossa, running transversely along the ends of the globular processes and the lower edges of the maxillary processes, serves to separate the upper lip from the gingival ridge along which the teeth are to develop, and a similar groove on the upper surface of the mandibular processes does the same for the lower jaw.

Normally the meeting surfaces of the various processes which form the face should have fused at the end of the second month. The fusion of the rounded globular processes causes a broad groove with raised edges, called the philtrum, in the center of the upper lip, which, with the two mandibular processes and two maxillary processes, divides the oral rim into five distinct areas and gives to the infantile mouth its pentagonal shape.[7] The other clefts between the various processes should close without a trace; failure to close properly is the cause of most facial anomalies.

Anomalies of the face. By far the most common of these is harelip (Fig. 4), caused by nonunion of the globular and maxillary processes, with cleft from mouth to nostril.[8] This condition may be single (i.e., on one side only) or double, and may be superficial, affecting the lip only, or deep, including the gingival ridge and the palate, but cleft palate may exist without harelip. The globular process normally carries the median and lateral incisor teeth, but in certain cases of harelip the line of cleavage runs between them. In fact, the congenital absence of one lateral incisor may represent a minor form of harelip.

As a rare variation the globular and maxillary processes may meet at one point only and then withdraw, leaving a bridge of

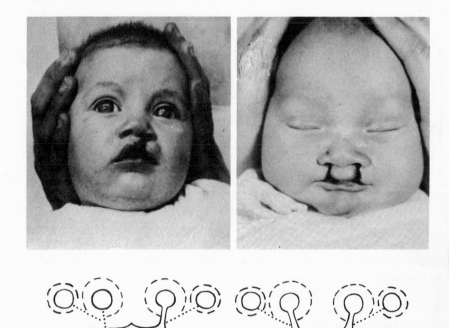

Fig. 4. Harelip, single and double (Ladd), with explanatory diagrams.

epithelium-covered connective tissue (Simonart's band) across the persisting cleft. Recent writers stress the relative lack of activity in the underlying mesoderm in any such withdrawal.

In double harelip the two globular processes may rotate anteriorly so that the incisors point forward. Median harelip, which most closely resembles the condition found in the hare, is a much rarer anomaly. It may involve merely the lip—nonunion of the two globular processes—or may affect also the lower part of the nose, with separation of the nostrils. The deep form includes median cleft palate and absence of the nasal septum.[9]

Oblique facial fissure (Fig. 5) extending from mouth to eye is a much more disfiguring condition. It is of two types, in one of which the fissure starts from the mouth as a lateral harelip, includes the naris, and continues to the inner canthus of the eye, while in the other the fissure starts from a point on the lip somewhat lateral to the philtrum and runs directly to the lower lid lateral to the inner

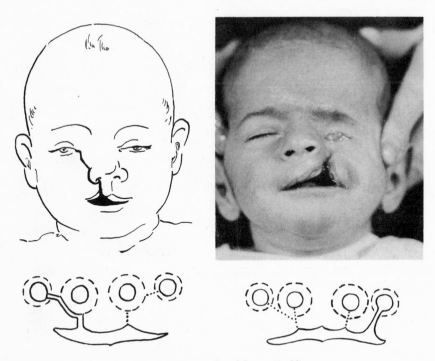

Fig. 5. Transverse facial fissure (Ladd).

canthus. In the first case there is a partial nonunion of the maxillary and globular processes in addition to a shallow groove along the line of the nasolachrymal duct, while in the other the cleft follows the original groove from eyeball to stomodaeum, which has been preserved by the failure of the maxillary process to complete its growth to the globular process, thus permitting the flat portion of the lateral nasal process to grow down between them and add its share to the upper lip. The nasolachrymal duct remains undisturbed in either type of oblique facial cleft.

Even more spectacular is the presence of a unilateral proboscis, with nasal pit at its tip, projecting from the brow above the inner canthus of one eye (Fig. 6). The nasal passage and internal naris are absent, and the olfactory placode of course functionless. This condition is due to the maldevelopment of the median and lateral nasal processes of one side, with the consequent absence of the corresponding globular process. To replace this lacking tissue, the

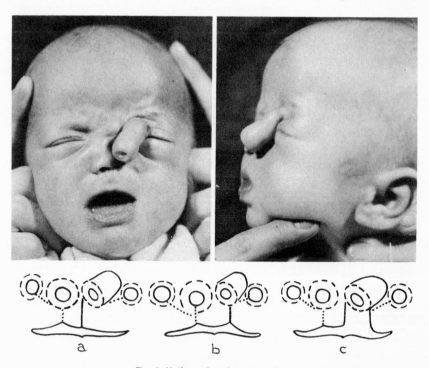

Fig. 6. Unilateral proboscis (Ladd).

remaining median nasal and globular processes may expand across the median line to meet the contralateral maxillary process at the usual place, i.e., without more than the normal extension of the latter (*b*); this seems to have occurred in the infant whose photograph is shown here, for without this normally placed suture the philtrum and upper lip notches would be uneven. On the other hand, the homolateral maxillary process may meet the opposite globular process in or near the midline, with resulting unevenness of the lip (*a*), or finally the vacant globular space may remain unfilled, causing a wide gap in upper lip and jaw (*c*).

A median proboscis, with single nasal pit of varying depth, is caused by the absence of the median nasal field and both median nasal processes. The two lateral nasal processes unite and alone constitute the protruding member; the nasal pits have fused. As in the lateral form, the proboscis is above the eyes in the upright face, as can be readily understood by remembering that the latter grow laterally from the side of the forebrain, while the nasal placodes develop in relation with the forward-growing outgrowths of the forebrain, the cerebral hemispheres. In the void below or caudal to the proboscis the eyes fuse more or less completely because of the lack of median tissue. The classical monster, Cyclops, with a single eye in the middle of his forehead above the normal nose, is embryologically a mythical impossibility.[10] On the other hand, extreme asymmetry of the two sides of the face may simulate this condition. Minor facial asymmetry can frequently be recognized in otherwise normal individuals, but in the absence of the unpaired medial field the two sets of nasal processes, right and left, may meet so asymmetrically that the nasal processes of one side, in the form of a proboscis, lie caudal to those of the other, and even caudal to the contralateral eye, which therefore seems to be in the classical relation cranial to the nose, though actually caudal to its homolateral proboscis. It is interesting to note that cyclopia in fish embryos can be produced at will by chemical or other means.[11]

Very rarely one of the olfactory placodes may be subdivided, and two nasal pits be formed on one side, separated by a thin septum. Three nostrils will then be present. One or both portions of the divided pit may develop imperfectly and remain as a blind pouch. This abnormality is probably the expression of a minimal amount of twinning; the nose, being the most anterior sense organ, is the first to show the effect of anterior longitudinal splitting.

From the second to the sixth intrauterine month the nares, both external and internal, are normally closed by epithelial plugs, which are resolved before birth. Rarely an internal plug may remain, become organized, and form a membranous veil blocking the passage. A similar condition is occasionally found in the trachea or bronchi at birth, and seems to be common to all air passages. In the posterior nares the surrounding bone may extend into the membranous veil, making a solid block. On the lateral wall of each nasal passage caudal to the vestibule, several irregular mounds grow inward, which by consolidation and enlargement become the thin nasal turbinates, curved overhanging shelves of bone covered by nonsensory glandular mucosa, chiefly of use to increase the area of the moist surface, so that the inspired air may be thoroughly moistened and warmed before entering the lungs. Still later in fetal life and continuing into the early postnatal months the same lateral wall and the roof of each nasal passage send out hollow epithelial diverticula which enter the cancellous portion of the neighboring still membranous bones of the skull and there spread widely as the various paranasal sinuses, many of which do not reach their full proportions until middle age. Variation in the shape or size of the frontal or maxillary sinuses may perhaps affect the form of the face, but can hardly be thought to lead to any facial anomaly.

Very rarely also the lower jaw may show anomalies in the form of a median cleft of the lip or of chin or of the entire mandible, or, much less spectacularly, of paired paramedian transverse clefts [12, 13] or tiny tubular tracts or fistulae in the lower lip, opening on the mucosal surface (Fig. 7) and either running to the inner surface opposite the incisor teeth or ending blindly somewhere along that route. The median clefts are understandable as arrests of development; the fistulae depend on the shape of the mandibular processes and in particular on the presence or absence of paired globular tips on the mandibular processes, similar to those of the median nasal processes (Fig. 3, a). A survey of many drawings of human embryos in the second month shows great variation in this respect—even young embryos often display distinctive characteristics. When present, these rounded tips may lead to the slightly cleft or dimpled

Fig. 7. Fistula of lower lip.

chin. On the inner side of the lower lip a particularly deep groove between the globular end and the main portion of the mandibular process may close over only superficially, the depth of the groove remaining open and making a deep mucous pit in the labial mucosa or even a fistula opening within the labial fossa,[14] opposite the lower lateral incisor. This is a rare occurrence, and may be bilateral. Similar mucous pits in the upper lip have not been reported.

Stomodaeum. The mammalian mouth is not strictly comparable to the stomodaeum of the early embryo, for the term stomodaeum refers to the depression of the surface ectoderm to meet the entoderm of the foregut at the oral plate, whereas the human mouth cavity comprises the additional space bounded by the forward growth of the maxillary and mandibular processes and also includes much of the pharynx. With the early degeneration of the oral plate, the mouth and pharynx become one continuous cavity, with no distinguishing change in the epithelial lining. The limits of the stomodaeum may, however, be outlined by the position on its walls of certain structures of known ectodermal origin, but no definite line can be drawn as a boundary. The teeth (enamel) are of ectoderm and hence all within the mouth proper, yet the tongue, as shown in the next chapter, though it projects between them, belongs for the greater part to the pharynx. The three main pairs of oral glands —parotid, submaxillary, and sublingual—show by the position of the orifices of their ducts that they also are ectodermal in origin. The tonsils and Eustachian tubes are both pharyngeal in origin and hence entodermal. The boundary stone on the upper wall is normally lost, but may return in a certain type of anomaly. In the young embryo a hollow dorsal outgrowth of the ectoderm, called Rathke's pouch, develops just in front of the oral plate and extends toward the floor of the forebrain, which sends a downgrowth to meet it. Together they form the anterior and posterior lobes of the pituitary gland. The pouch becomes stalked and the stalk is then normally lost, but at birth there is commonly present a minute canal through the body of the sphenoid bone which marks its former path. Remnants of the stalk, forming accessory anterior lobe nodules, may rarely be found along the canal or at its two ends, either in the soft parts at the dome of the anatomical pharynx (where they again supply a visible boundary mark) or above the floor of the sella turcica (suprasellar). A tumor or cyst arising from such remnants is known as a craniopharyngioma. From a strictly embryological point of view, it might be well to return to the older name, Rathke's-pouch tumor, or to coin the term "craniostomatoma," to indicate its derivation from the ectoderm of the primitive stomodaeum.

Occasionally such a cyst or tumor derived from the original stalk of the anterior lobe of the pituitary gland may become large enough to cause grave symptoms, which vary with its position. An expanding mass at the lower end of the canal may interfere seriously with breathing by blocking the choanae; at the upper end of the canal, in the sella Turcica, supracellar, it may press on the pituitary gland or on the optic chiasma, with signs of endocrine and visual disturbance, or, if very large, may cause symptoms of intracranial pressure. In a few cases the tumor or the wall of a cyst, as though to emphasize its ectodernal origin, contains one or more hard modules composed of cells similar to those of the tooth germs; this condition is known as an adamantinoma or ameloblastoma.[15] In the larger of these tumors calcification and osteogenesis are common, perhaps representing the dentine component of the tooth.

The external ear, or auricle, develops around the first branchial cleft, which limits caudally the mandibular process. A raised rim develops around the cleft in much the same way as around the nasal pit, but in this case the rim takes the form of a series of small mounds or hillocks, three on each side of the linear cleft (Fig. 3). They extend along almost the whole length of the cleft, and therefore at first (during the fifth or sixth week) reach nearly to the midline ventrally, but with the growth and expansion of the mandibular processes, and especially of the angles of the lower jaws, they are forced dorsally to the side of the head. The hillocks vary in size and position in individual embryos, and descriptions of their future development, probably because of this variation, also differ as to the precise contributions made by the six mounds to the formation of the named parts of the adult auricle.[16]

Variations in the size and shape of the ear are definitely inherited; in addition to these minor changes, actual malformations or anomalies may occur. Both ears may remain in the original position near the midline ventrally because of the lack of mandibular growth; this condition is called synotus. One or both ears may be represented by a few separate tabs of skin-covered cartilage. Similar tabs, slightly lower in the neck and nearer the midline, represent the anomalous attempt at auricle formation around the second cleft (p. 26).

Of quite different character are the anomalous fistulae and epithelial pits in and around the external auditory meatus. Two neighboring auricular mounds may grow to mushroom shape and, as the overhanging sides unite, leave a covered fistula or deep epithelial pocket beneath them, similar to the mucous pits or fistulae of the lower lip already described. Complete fistulae from the skin may open within the meatus at various depths; in other cases, because the mounds project over the edge of the cleft, the pits may extend from the meatus toward the surface without reaching the skin. Another group of deep blind pockets or of patent fistulae from the meatus may run down behind the jaw perhaps for an inch or more and these either end blindly or open to the surface. This group is due to the faulty closure of the lower part of the original cleft, drawn out by the dorsal migration of the auricle. Variants of all these types can be expected.

The first cleft may be absent on one or both sides, either as the result of primary agenesis or because, failing to meet the first pouch from within, the young cleft flattens out and disappears. In these cases, both the external auditory meatus and the tympanic membrane are absent, and probably the middle-ear cavity will be small and the mastoid process deficient. But with these internal conditions, irregular mounds or tabs of skin containing cartilage bars may be present to represent the absent auricle. The internal ear is usually unaffected, as shown by the fact that balance is preserved and that the organ of Corti responds to stimulation through bone conduction.

2 ———

PHARYNX AND NECK

In an embryo of about four weeks, the cranial end of the foregut, called the pharynx, lies between the hindbrain dorsally and the heart ventrally. It is widely expanded cranially, where, after the rupture of the oral membrane, it is continuous with the oral cavity, but narrows caudally to join the slender oesophagus; the roof is vaulted and highest just caudal to Rathke's pouch. The most striking characteristic is the presence along its two sides of four pairs of slender pouches (Fig. 10), growing out to meet four pairs of corresponding ingrowing clefts along the sides of the neck (Figs. 1 and 9). The first three pairs of these pharyngeal pouches, at the point of meeting with the clefts, form closing membranes of fused pouch entoderm and skin ectoderm, similar to the oral membrane; the fourth pouches never reach the surface and hence, in man, form no closing plates. The pouches and clefts represent the gill slits of fishes (Fig. 8), but in mammals the plates do not normally rupture and the pouches serve other purposes than that of oxygen exchange. Between the successive pouches and corresponding clefts the masses of tissue extending from top to bottom of the head are called the branchial arches. The first arch, in front of the first pouch and cleft, is the mandibular arch, the same that has been already studied as the mandibular process, from which the lower jaw develops; the second, between the first and second pouches, is the hyoid arch. On the lateral surface of these two arches grow the mounds from which the auricle is formed. For these reasons the first cleft is called variously the mandibular, hyomandibular, or auricular cleft; the second arch is the hyoid arch, and the others are usually mentioned merely by number.

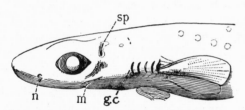

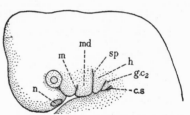

Fig. 8. Head of a young dogfish: *g.c.*, gill cleft; *m*, mouth; *n*, nasal pit; *sp*, spiracle (first cleft). [From J. L. Bremer, *Textbook of histology* (Blakiston, Philadelphia, ed. 5, 1936).]

Fig. 9. Head of human embryo of 10 mm: *c.s.*, cervicle sinus; *g. c. 2*, second branchial cleft; *h*, hyoid arch; *sp*, spiracle (first cleft); *md*, mandibular process; *m*, mouth; *n*, nasal pit. [From J. L. Bremer, *Textbook of histology* (Blakiston, Philadelphia, ed 5, 1936).]

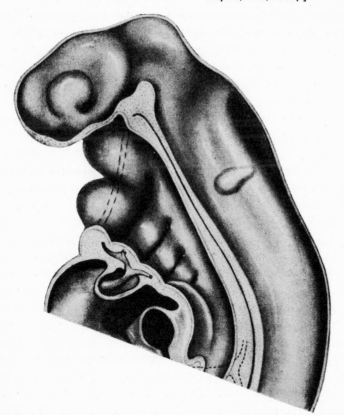

Fig. 10. Reconstruction of the head of a human embryo of 4.2 mm (3 weeks), showing right lateral wall of pharynx, with pouches (after His). [From J. L. Bremer and H. L. Weatherford, *Textbook of histology* (Blakiston Div., McGraw-Hill, New York, ed. 6, 1944).]

The branchial arches offer pathways for a series of paired arteries, the aortic arches, running from the ventral to the dorsal walls of the pharynx. Each first aortic arch traverses a mandibular arch, each second aortic arch passes through a hyoid arch, and so forth, the original five pairs of aortic arches being separated from each other by the four pairs of pharyngeal pouches and clefts. Also through these arches run the successive nerves of the hindbrain, and within them are developed the cartilages of the visceral skeleton: Meckel's cartilage (later incorporated in the bone of the lower jaw) in each first arch, the lesser cornu of the hyoid bone in the second, the greater cornu in the third, the thyroid and cricoid cartilages in the fourth and fifth arches, respectively.

At first the clefts are arrayed in regular sequence along the side of the head, like the gill silts of the shark, but as the neck bend takes place the second, third, and fourth clefts (as well as the pouches within) are crowded at their ventral ends (Fig. 9). This is reflected in the converging horns of the hyoid bone. The three crowded clefts are then all covered in by the overhanging growth of the second arch acting as an operculum, so that they now open on a sunken pit, called the cervical sinus, to which there is only a single linear opening to the surface in the position of the fourth cleft. The action is similar to that which buries the Island of Reil in the brain. Sometimes, in an embryo in which the neck bend is less pronounced, the third arch forms the operculum, the second cleft remaining as a separate entity. The opercular cleft normally closes by the middle of the second month and the resulting enclosed cervical sinus is obliterated soon afterward. The last point of closure is normally at the ventral end of the operculum, but may be at any part of the line.

The pharyngeal pouches also are arranged in a special pattern (Fig. 10); the first pair are longest and point dorsally as well as laterally, the second point directly laterally, and the third and fourth pairs are progressively shorter, arise from a more ventral portion of the lateral pharyngeal wall, and are more ventrally directed. The fourth pair branch and the lower branches, pointing caudally, are known as the ultimobranchial or postbranchial bodies. In line with these pouches, but from a more caudal portion of the foregut and from the median ventral wall, arises a single outgrowth, the lung bud, which is to form both lungs. From the lung bud, stretching cranially into the pharynx as far forward as the ventral ends of the third branchial arches, a median longitudinal hollow ridge or keel gradually develops on the pharyngeal floor. This structure is apparently the result of pressure from the expanding ventral ends of the last three pairs of arches on the ventrolateral walls of the originally tubular pharynx, for the resulting shape of this cavity resembles, in transverse section, the capital letter T, the thin keel forming the upright and the curved horizontal member representing the flattened dorsal portion of the cavity. As will be seen in the following chapter, the keel is to become the trachea, the dorsal portion the oesophagus, while in the ventral ends of the branchial arches the skeleton of the larynx is formed.

Each first pouch passes up in the mesenchyma between the skin and the buried otocyst and, becoming narrower, forms the Eustachian tube. By expansion at its distal end, it makes the tympanic cavity, across which a column of mesenchyma remains to become the chain of ossicles; by continued expansion after birth the mastoid cells are hollowed out. The closing plate, with the addition of an ingrowth of mesenchyma between its two layers, eventually serves as the lower part of the tympanic membrane. The second pair of pouches is usually said to remain shallow, to withdraw from its closing plate, and to lodge the palatine tonsils in the caudal portion of their wide inner ends, leaving the cranial portion vacant and flaring, as the supratonsillar fossa. This is, however, hardly an accurate statement, for before tonsil formation begins the lateral half of each second pouch is drawn out, as the neck thickens, into a long slender tube reaching to the closing plate. The tubular portion, in normal development, breaks down and disappears, and it is in the wider shallow remainder of the original pouch that the tonsil develops.[1] If, abnormally, the slender tubular portion remains in whole or in part, it forms the basis of some of the rarer anomalies mentioned below. The third pouch near its lateral tip sends a tubular diverticulum from its caudal wall down the neck in front of the pharynx into the thorax, where it meets and fuses with its fellow of the opposite side to form the thymus (Fig. 11). The diverticulum becomes solid and loses connection with its parent pouch. The fourth pouch produces a similar, but much smaller, diverticulum which follows the same course and adds its mass also to the thymus.

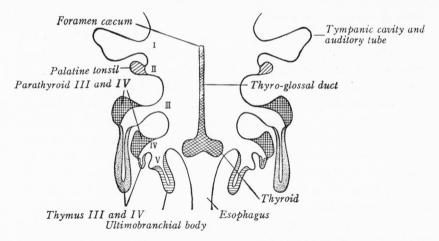

Fig. 11. Diagram of pharyngeal derivatives (Weatherford).

The cranial walls of the third and fourth pouches also produce near their tips solid nodules which are to form the parathyroid bodies and join the thyroid gland as parathyroids III and IV. The remains of the tubular pouches normally disappear by being absorbed into the wall of the growing pharynx. The fate of the ultimobranchial bodies seems to vary in different animals; they join the thyroid gland in some, the thymus in others, but in man they are generally considered to degenerate completely.[2]

The pharynx produces also a median outgrowth. From the floor between the first and second pair of branchial pouches a tubular structure grows ventrally and then caudally in front of the pharynx in the future neck to the level of the fourth pair of pouches, where it branches and produces the thyroid gland,[3] the follicles of which are isolated sections of the original tube. The pharyngeal opening of the tube or duct is later found on the surface of the tongue and the duct is hence known as the thyroglossal duct. Normally it disappears, except for a blind depression on the tongue, the foramen caecum, and for its caudal end, where it may form the pyramidal lobe of the thyroid gland.

In the case of any ductless organ with a developmental history of outgrowth and subsequent obliteration of a parent duct, or of extensive migration, anomalous rests may remain anywhere along the course of the growth. These may take the form of accessory glands, of vesicular fragments of the original tube, or of gland nodules in the walls of cysts. Bits of thyroid gland or closed cysts may be found near the foramen caecum or anywhere in the course of the thyroglossal duct, or in the anterior part of the tongue, having been carried out of the original line by the forward growth of that organ. A thyroglossal fistula, opening on the ventral surface of the neck, is probably due to pathological erosion, but may possibly represent an anomalous branch of the thyroglossal duct, which reaches the surface, forms a closing plate, and then ruptures. In the same way accessory thymic nodules or cysts may be found in the lower part of the neck, and accessory or abnormally placed parathyroid glands are not uncommon. The same holds true in the case of the anterior lobe of the pituitary body, which grows dorsally from the roof of the oral cavity to meet the posterior lobe, then becomes stalked and finally ductless. Along the course of the stalk, from sella turcica to mouth, anterior-lobe nodules may infrequently be found.

The tongue is formed in a complex manner.[4] The branchial arches continue ventrally and meet in the floor of the mouth and pharynx. At 4 weeks, just in front of the foramen caecum and from the first and second arches of both sides, a single median rounded mound, the tuberculum impar, develops and grows forward (Fig. 12). Formerly this was supposed to spead forward into the oral cavity and form the whole anterior portion or body of the tongue. Now it is known that in man the tuberculum impar is impinged upon by paired swellings from the two mandibular arches, which enlarge, meet in the midline over the tuberculum, and grow forward to form the entire body of the organ. Irregularities in the growth and fusion of these three parts may cause a bifid or trifid tongue, and may also explain the rare median-line or lateral lingual cysts or longitudinal tubular sinuses in the substance of the tongue, which occasionally occur. The posterior part, or root, of the tongue develops similarly from a median mound, the copula, derived from the ventral ends of the second and third arches, and from lateral swellings of these arches which grow caudally and cover in most of the copula, until only its caudal tip remains as the epiglottis. The line of demarcation between the body of the tongue and its root is probably just behind the rows of vallate papillae coming to a point just in front of the foramen caecum (Fig. 13). The lateral swellings of the various arches

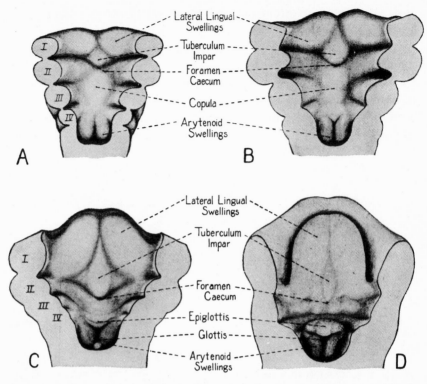

Fig. 12. Four stages in the development of the tongue; the upper part of the head has been cut away to show the floor of the oropharynx; cut pharyngeal arches are numbered post-orally A, 4–5 mm; B, mm; C, 8–9 mm; D, 15 mm. [From B. M. Pattern, *Human embryology* (Blakiston Div., McGraw-Hill, New York, ed. 2, 1953).]

actually supply only the mucosal covering of the various parts of the tongue, and to this mucosa the appropriate nerves traversing these arches contribute sensory or visceral (glandular) branches; the lingual muscles grow forward into the tongue from the more caudal somatic mesoderm and carry with them their own nerves, grouped together as the hypoglossal nerves. The bulk of the tongue reduces the cavity of the closed mouth and anterior pharynx to a transversely curved slit.

On the dorsal surface of the posterior part of the tongue a broad field of tonsillar crypts, interspersed with mucous glands, constitutes the lingual tonsil. A similar broad area on the dorsal dome of the nasopharynx is called the pharyngeal tonsil or "the adenoids"; the close proximity of this group to the pharyngeal openings of the Eustachian tube puts the latter passages in real danger of being blocked by overgrowth or pathological swelling of the lymphoid tissue. These two tonsillar fields, together with the paired palatine tonsils lodged in the second pouches, form a nearly continuous protective ring at the entrance to the lungs and intestinal tract.

From the lateral floor of the mouth and from the inner surfaces of the adjoining cheeks the various salivary glands grow out, during

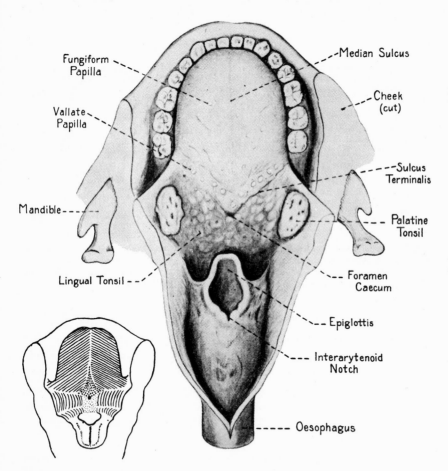

Fig. 13. Tongue, floor of mouth, and pharyngeal region of adult. Pharynx cut away to expose epiglottis and entrance to larynx. Small sketch suggests the parts of the tongue of different embryological origin. [From B. M. Patten, *Human embryology* (Blakiston Div., McGraw-Hill, New York, ed. 2, 1953).]

the eighth and ninth weeks, as solid cords, later canalized. As in the lungs, the subsequent branches of these cords retain their duct type of epithelial lining during the greater part of fetal life, the active end-pieces (alveoli or acini) appearing late, in the lungs at about 6 months, in the salivary glands not until late in the first postnatal year. Until the proper glandular units develop, the digestive enzymes for carbohydrates are absent, although the ducts may produce an abundant mucous secretion. In these days of predigested baby foods in glass jars, it is pleasant to remember the Negro mammies, by instinct or from age-old tribal custom, feeding the infants in their charge mouthfuls of bread already well chewed in their own mouths.

In later embryonic life, the structures in the pharyngeal region are affected by the straightening of the neck bend and consequent lifting of the head. Those structures ventrally situated shift caudally in relation to the dorsal parts. The thymus is carried down into the thorax, the thyroid gland less far. The line of fusion of the opercular lips now slants sharply caudally, extending from the level of the tonsil (second pouch) almost to the clavicle in the front of the neck. The cervical sinus, if it has not already been obliterated, is drawn out as a long tube beneath the skin along this line. Still another influence is at work. The skin of the lateral surface of the embryo has a tendency to shift forward, because its chief growth is from the back. This is shown by the adult position of the nipples, for these develop from the "milk line," which in the embryo runs from axilla to groin, and moves ventrally with growth. This tendency may cause the opercular line, carrying any surviving part of the sinus with it, to curve forward with growth nearly to the midventral line.

In a region of such active change affecting so many structures, various types of anomaly are to be expected. Malformations of the auricle (first cleft) have been considered in the previous chapter. Very rarely a fistula of the middle ear may be caused by abnormal extension of the tympanic cavity to the surface of the head behind the auricle, with the formation and then the rupture of an additional closing plate, as in the case of the thyroglossal fistula; the Eustachian tube prolongs the fistula to the pharynx. By a similar rupture of any of the other closing plates, the pouches may open from pharynx to skin. This condition is called perforating pharyngeal fistula. The lining layer of the fistula in these instances is in part pharyngeal membrane, in part the skin of the cervical sinus (Fig. 14, *A*), since the closing plates of these pouches are situated within this depression; to reach the surface of the neck, the rupture of the closing plate must be accompanied by the incomplete closure of the cervical sinus. The whole fistula then includes the pharyngeal pouch, the ruptured closing plate, and the open cervical sinus. The surface opening of any of the three pouches may be at any point along the opercular line; a perforating fistula of the second pouch may form an exception to this rule, for in those rare instances in which the third (instead of the second) arch forms the operculum for the cervical sinus, a perforating fistula of the second pouch will reach the surface along the course of the second cleft, which corresponds in position with the cranial border of the lesser cornu of the hyoid bone within.

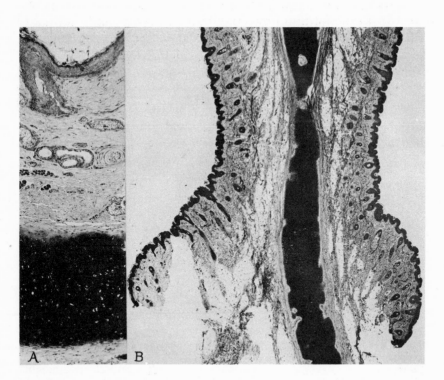

Fig. 14. Sections of (A) wall of a cervical sinus fistula and (B) of a "wattle," from outer edge of second cleft. Note epidermis and cartilage. From infants.

Perforating pharyngeal fistulae, affording an open passage between the pharynx and the surface of the neck, are relatively rare; much more commonly the originally continuous tube is broken at one or more points. The tube may extend inward a longer or shorter distance from the skin, ending blindly, or sections of the pouch-cleft tract may be cut off, leaving closed vesicles or cysts along its course. A true open fistula of the second pouch must be very uncommon in any case, for the growth of the tonsil normally blocks its inner end; the lateral portion of the pouch together with the cervical sinus may, however, form a narrow blind tube extending from the surface of the neck to the base of the tonsil (Fig. 15).

The normal presence of cartilage around the edges of the first clefts, as shown in the concha of the ear, and its occasional presence around the second cleft and the whole cervical sinus in the form of irregular plaques or projecting tabs has already been mentioned (p. 15). In the form of projecting tabs this condition is normal in the goat, where the paired cartilage-bearing appendages are known as "wattles," and in the moose, in which the paired projections

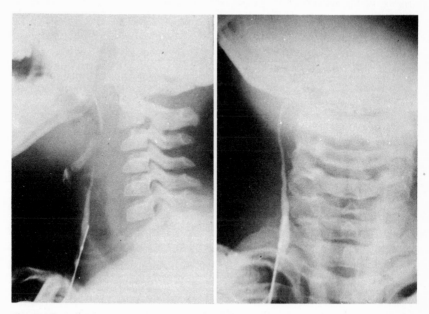

Fig. 15. Deep fistula of second pharyngeal pouch, opening just above clavicle; pouch and sinus. Anterior and lateral views (Neuhauser).

fuse, as the "bell." Cases showing both the fistula and the "wattle" have been found in human infants (Fig. 14).

Often it is possible to tell from which pouch a fistula is derived by simple reasoning: thus, the second pharyngeal pouch lies above the third branchial arch, through which runs an artery which is to be transformed into the proximal segment of the internal carotid artery (p. 171). A deep fistula of this pouch must, therefore, cross cranial to this segment, that is, above the carotid notch; a fistula of the third pouch runs below it. The vesicles may be from the pharyngeal pouch or from the sinus, or may include both pouch and sinus, in the absence of the closing plate. The latter condition may sometimes be recognized by the presence of two distinctive types of lining epithelium, pharyngeal for pouch, skin for sinus, but commonly all such characteristics will be destroyed by the internal pressure of the increasing enclosed fluid.

In the case of cysts or short tubules lying close beneath the skin it is usually impossible to determine from which pouch they originated, for they are superficial to all landmarks and the shifts in position by which they are influenced may have moved them far from their original levels. Fortunately, the question is largely academic, for it has been found that in operating for the removal of either a branchiogenic fistula or a cyst, no matter how superficial, it is wise to search for and remove any other remaining portion of the whole tract that might cause future trouble, even though this entails a wide dissection of the neck.*

* Bruce Proctor, "Lateral vestigial cysts and fistulas of the neck," *Laryngoscope 65,* 355–401 (1955).

3 ——

TRACHEA, BRONCHI, AND LUNGS

The first indication of the development of the lungs is the appearance at about four weeks of the lung bud, a median ventral outgrowth of the foregut, a short distance behind the last pair of pharyngeal pouches. This position suggests that the lung bud may be considered as the most caudal pair of branchial pouches which, following the ever more ventral trend of the successive pouches as they leave the pharyngeal wall, have finally met and fused in the median ventral line, ready to take over the function of breathing given up by the gills. The bud is the terminal enlargement of the keellike ventral portion of the caudal end of the pharynx (Fig. 16, A), and although primarily single it rapidly shows its double nature by producing two lateral pouches, the primary bronchi, from which the two lungs are derived.

In fetal and postnatal life the two bronchi are joined to the pharynx by the trachea, which thus appears as the main duct of the pulmonary system, but, unlike the main duct of most compound glands, the trachea does not itself grow out and lengthen; instead, the whole caudal portion of the pharynx below the fourth pair of pouches and including the ventral keel grows rapidly longer, carrying the lung bud far below the pouches (Fig. 16, B). The lumen of the lengthened portion then assumes the shape of a narrow, laterally compressed slit (C), which is soon divided from below upward into two tubes, the oesophagus dorsally and the trachea ventrally, the latter leading to the bronchi (D). The division is accomplished by the folding in of the lateral walls of the foregut until they meet and fuse, thus turning the slitlike cavity into two

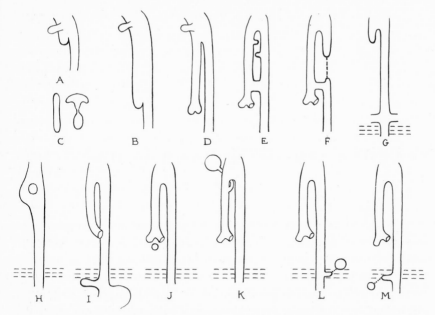

Fig. 16. Diagrams of the development of the trachea and its anomalies: (A–D) development of trachea; (E) traction diverticula and (F) tracheo-oesophageal fistula; (G, H) agenesis of trachea; (G and I–M) misplaced or supernumerary bronchi, some subdiaphragmatic; (K) tracheocele. The position of the fourth pouch is indicated in (A), (B), (C).

parallel channels, which are soon separated by the degeneration of the fused walls, thus freeing the two parallel tubes, joined only above at the larynx.

Tracheo-oesophageal fistula.[1] This method of subdividing a single tube is common in embryological development, and lends itself readily to the production of anomalies. The same result can be accomplished by the growth within a tube of paired linear ridges. Irregularities in the surface of a fold may lead to traction diverticula, blind pockets from the dorsal wall of the trachea or the ventral wall of the oesophagus (Fig. 16, *E*), while a transverse groove or deep gap in the surface of one or both of the folds results in the anomalous connection or fistula between the two resulting tubes. Tracheo-oesophageal fistula may occur at any level below the larynx, but the most common site is at or just above the tracheal bifurcation. Occasionally the oesophagus opens into a bronchus. Both tubes may remain open though joined,[2] but more commonly the oesophagus is closed just above the fistula, as though the folds had turned abruptly dorsally at this point, and the lower section, with the fistula, may be carried away from the upper by the continued lengthening of the pharynx, though the two blind ends are often connected by a fibrous strand (*F*). Thereafter the upper section may make more or less growth, according to individual circumstances, and the gap between the severed ends of the oesophagus, upper and lower, may be correspondingly shorter or longer. Through such a fistula air may enter the stomach, or, if the oesophagus remains continuous, ingested food may enter the lungs. With interrupted oesophagus, food lodges in the upper oesophageal pouch and can reach the stomach only by way of the trachea.

In the lower tracheo-oesophageal fistulae just described the paired lateral folds turn dorsally, cutting through the oesophagus. Another group of anomalies is reported,[3] in which the folds must have turned ventrally. In these cases the trachea is completely severed at an early date, being represented only by the larynx, which either ends blindly or joins the upper oesophagus (Fig. 16, *G, H*). In one instance, both bronchi were transferred to the oesophagus and by the lengthening of the latter were carried down nearly to the diaphragm (*G*), where they developed relatively normal lungs; in another, the bronchi and lungs failed to develop (bilateral agenesis of the lungs). In still another case the folds must have run obliquely, separating the bronchial buds, the left bud remaining with the trachea and producing a large left lung, the right bud being transferred to the oesophagus and appearing as a subdiaphragmatic blind tube or cyst (Fig. 16, *I*). Though arising from the oesophagus, these displaced bronchi retain their normal ciliated epithelium and mucosa, but usually are of small caliber.

The deflection of the dividing septum either dorsally or ventrally is not the only suggested cause of these anomalies comprising, with the tracheo-oesophageal fistula, the discontinuity of either the oesophagus or the trachea. The stenosis of the oesophagus in the normal solid stage of the mucosa (p. 59) has been called upon to explain the upper blind oesophageal pouch, but it is now known that in the oesophagus the lumen is probably never completely occluded, and severance of this tube into upper and lower segments, while common with the accompanying tracheo-oesophageal fistula, is almost unknown without it. Moreover, this suggestion would not apply to those cases in which the trachea is interrupted, since in this tube there is no solid stage. Another suggestion rests on the course of the anomalous right subclavian artery of low origin (p. 179). This vessel arises from the aortic arch distal to the root of the left subclavian artery and passes either dorsal to the oesophagus or between oesophagus and trachea, often indenting the dorsal wall of one or the other; very rarely it runs ventral to the trachea. Excessive indentation might result in the interruption of either tube; that this should occur only in conjunction with the fistula still lacks explanation.

The term *accessory* or *supernumerary bronchus* may refer either to a primary (stem) bronchus or to an extra intrapulmonary branch of the bronchial tree. In the latter case the extra branch may produce an accessory lobe, or if growth does not ensue may remain as a blind diverticulum, occasionally recognizable by roentgen ray; or it may lose its connection and persist as a closed cyst within the lung,[4] or even as a vesicle within the pleural cavity, either free (Fig. 16, *J*) or attached by a pedicle to the visceral pleura,[5] the attachment revealing its intrapulmonary origin. The primary extrapulmonary accessory bronchi may develop either from the trachea or, much less frequently, from the oesophagus, as explained in the preceding paragraph. They may arise at any level and from either side (*L, M*). In the embryo they are more numerous than after birth, showing that some of them are absorbed into the growing walls of the parent stem. Those that persist may remain tubular, may be cut off as cysts, or may progress to recognizable lung tissue, but all can be recognized by the bronchial or pulmonary mucosa, whether they stem from trachea or oesophagus, unless the character of the mucosa has been lost by internal pressure (within a cyst) or by erosion. Bronchial musculature and cartilage may or may not be present.

These accessory bronchi and cysts have a wide distribution, and this is due to the fact that at the time of their first appearance (5 or 6 weeks) the trachea and oesophagus lie in a mass of loose mesenchyma through which the new buds may penetrate readily. The tissue here is to become the mediastinum and is continuous into the root of the neck, the dorsal wall of the chest, and the septum transversum, which last is to form the tendinous center of the diaphragm. The accessory bronchi may, therefore, grow into any of these regions, where they may be found as cysts or as masses of atelectatic lung, free or attached by tube or pedicle. Bronchial cysts have been reported behind the manubrium, near the suprarenal gland, in the diaphragm or coronary ligament, or in the septa within the liver. A common location for small cysts is at the bifurcation of the trachea, also called the bronchial carina * (Fig. 16, *J*). They may leave the diaphragm to invade the abdominal cavity or bulge the walls of the pleural cavity from the back, from the mediastinum, or from the diaphragm (*L, M*). One has been reported projecting from the edge of the ruptured diaphragm,[6] one as interfering with the closure of the pericardium;[7] and in one case in this hospital, an accessory bronchus penetrated the diaphragm and, below it, joined with an aberrant hepatic duct (p. 76). Only within the pleural cavity, where the developing tissue is subjected to the necessary alternating pressures, and only when derived from the trachea, can the lung growth of these accessory bronchi achieve full development as an accessory lung lobe, and this may occur here no matter from what wall the pleural cavity is entered; those from the oesophagus become atelectatic at birth. Only those which enter the pleural cavity near the root of the lung have the normal pulmonary blood supply; the others are served by the nearest branches of the systemic vessels. The arteries may come from the costal branches of the aorta or by extension of the oesophageal group, and the veins may lead to the superior vena cava either directly or through the azygos system.

The most bizarre form of accessory bronchus is the tracheocele,[8] that curious tumor which appears suddenly in the root of the neck, usually after violent coughing or vomiting, or following severe muscular strain in men or childbirth in women. The "tumor" has been present since before birth as a small inconspicuous cyst connected with the trachea by a slender tubular stalk (Fig. 16, *K*); excessive intratracheal pressure forces the air into the cyst and expands it in such a way that the air is entrapped. The expanded cyst is noticed as the "new" tumor.

---

* The word *carina* means "keel"; the term refers to the ridge between the two bronchi as seen by the broncoscopist. A vessel is careened when laid on its side until the keel is visible.

A somewhat similar "tumor" may be encountered within the lumen of the trachea, usually on the right side because of the presence of the oesophagus on the left (p. 46). In a recent case in this hospital the tracheal passage was seriously obstructed by a mass or cyst attached to the wall, yielding to the pressure of a probe, soft and fluctuant. On puncture, the cyst apparently disappeared as its delicate protruding wall settled down against the underlying tracheal mucosa with the escape of the contained air. This occurrence may perhaps be explained as due to the presence of a small accessory bronchus or tracheal diverticulum [9] which, because of a late start, failed to pierce the already present dense layers of the tracheal wall and hence ran for some distance within the submucosa (Fig. 17, a), its terminal expansion bulging into the lumen, lifting before it the local epithelium so that the free surface is composed of tracheal epithelium and cyst epithelium, back to back (b). The same condition could start from the faulty development and expansion of a tracheal mucosal gland (c), and similar intraluminal expansions of slender tubular diverticula are not infrequently seen in the intestinal tract. In the position shown in the drawing, inhalation would expose the tiny entrance to the cyst and tend to its further expansion, while exhalation, by moving the cyst orally, would close the duct and prevent the escape of air. Like a tracheocele, such cysts may remain unnoticed until excessive enlargement calls for intervention.

It will be noticed that the lower neck is a region where one may encounter cysts derived either from an accessory bronchus or from one of the pharyngeal pouches, and it is sometimes desirable to distinguish between the two origins. Frequently this is impos-

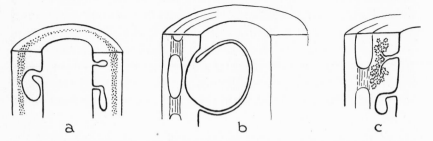

Fig. 17. Diagrams to show origin of intratracheal cyst from a diverticulum (a,b) or from a cystic tracheal gland (c).

sible, for the mucosa may have been so stretched and flattened by internal pressure or so badly eroded that its normal character cannot be recognized. The deep mucosal glands, which usually escape destruction, are similar in both pharynx and trachea, and the outer walls of both types may lack definite muscle layers. But the presence in certain cases of cartilage, of deep lobulation, or of recognizable lung alveoli, on the one hand, or of areas of skin epithelium (from the cervical sinus) in the wall of the bronchial cyst, on the other, renders the decision an easy matter.

Agenesis of one lung. In sharp contrast to the numerous forms of accessory bronchi and bronchial cysts, indicating a superabundant growth power in the tracheal system, are the much rarer instances of agenesis of a lung,[10] suggesting an inherent lack of developmental force. The condition may be recognized in infants by roentgen-ray studies after lipiodol injections[11] (Fig. 18), but occasionally is not noticed until after death.[12] In the remaining lung in these cases growth is accelerated, the mediastinum is forced to the affected side, and the heart may also be displaced or remain in its normal position, partially surrounded by the enlarged lobes of the remaining lung. The shape of the chest may or may not be noticeably

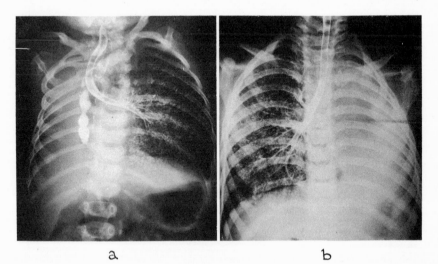

a   b

Fig. 18. Agenesis of one lung; roentgenograms of infants. Note displaced trachea and oesophagus in (a), caused by expansion of left upper lobe. [From C. F. Ferguson and E. B. D. Neuhauser, *Am. J. Roentgenol, and Radium Therapy* 52, 467 (1944).]

altered, but the dome of the diaphragm on the affected side is much elevated. Any remaining pleural space is filled with fluid or fat.

Each lung comprises all of the branches of a stem, or primary, bronchus, together with the vascular mesodermal tissue which surrounds them. The first few branchings of each primary bronchus take place with great regularity as to position and direction, and on them depend the characteristic lobation of the lungs; but even here occasional variations occur, producing anomalous lobes. The divisions of the secondary and tertiary bronchi are less regular but usually dichotomous, and successive divisions continue until in an embryo of 5 months there may be 10–15 generations of branches. So far, all these tubes are lined with the same type of low columnar epithelium; but in the next few generations a new type of growth makes its appearance, contrasting sharply with clear-cut tubular bronchi by being irregularly expanded and with thin walls, the flattened epithelium of which is closely surrounded by vascular mesenchyma. This is poorly fashioned "respiratory epithelium," and when it is present in sufficient amount the fetus becomes viable, usually during the sixth month.

The character of the alveolar wall is still the subject of dispute. To one group of investigators the surface of the alveolar cavities, like all other surfaces of the body, external or internal, is covered or lined by a continuous sheet of epithelial cells, resting on a fibrous or reticular base. The fact that such a continuous layer can seldom be demonstrated in the usual microscopic preparations of the lung is thought to be due to the extreme, filmlike thinness of portions of this epithelium. Such invisibly thin protoplasmic films are readily understandable by the physiological chemist and tacitly accepted in the common conception of the fat cell, in which the thin wall surrounding the fat globule is rarely continuously seen. Moreover, the films in both the fat cell and the alveolar wall can be made to swell to full visibility (Fig. 19, *C*) by immersion in some hypertonic solution,[13] and those in the alveoli have now also been visualized by electron microscopy.[14] Yet to another group of anatomists[15] the sudden change from the cuboidal epithelium of the terminal bronchioles to the apparently wallless air spaces indicates the rupture of the distal bronchiolar epithelium and the escape of air into the

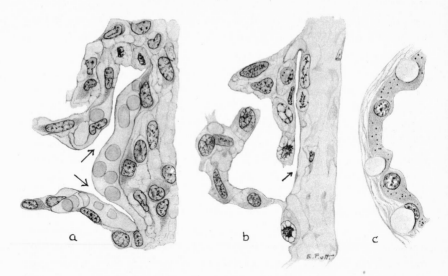

Fig. 19. Development of new alveoli by the growth of minute tubular sprouts into the surrounding mesenchymal tissue; note mitoses. (a) Normal rabbit fetus. (b) Remaining lung of kitten after lobectomy; arrows in latest alveoli point toward new sprouts. (c) Frozen section of lung of rat, after swelling by immersion in thymol; protoplasmic film lining alveolus (at right) made visible. In fresh specimen, protoplasmic particles showed Brownian movement. [From J. L. Bremer, J. Thoracic Surg. 6, 338 (1937).]

surrounding tissue spaces; the impinging capillaries are naked, or covered only by a reticular net. Whether in tissue space or film-lined alveolus, a thin sheet of fluid also covers the inner surface.[16] Like fish, we take our oxygen through water.

The cause of this flattening or rupture of the epithelium of the enlarged terminal tubes is not clear. Growth of the rib cage, fetal muscular movements, and the completion of the diaphragm may all play a part in creating a certain suction within the lung, and at birth lanugo hairs and a few epithelial scales from the skin of the fetus are often found in the lung cavities, brought there by the amniotic fluid inhaled by intrauterine respiration,[17] but the infrequency and irregularity of the fetal movements makes it doubtful whether the actual thinning of the cuboidal epithelium can be due to intrapulmonary pressure caused in this way. Certain fatty changes in the cells lining these terminal pulmonary branches have been reported, and these may aid in the flattening process. The expansion of the terminal branches and the change in epithelial type do not prevent continued growth by further branching, but the growth pattern is no longer dichotomous. As the expanded terminals, prototypes of the later alveolar ducts, distend still further, the walls between constricting bands of the surrounding connective tissue bulge out as alveoli, and from the angles and corners of these alveoli further generations of thin-walled spaces grow out as new branches of the bronchial tree, in the form of minute tubular sprouts with the same type of flattened epithelium,[18] pushing into the surrounding vascular mesoderm (Fig. 19, *B*); their active growth is frequently attested by the presence of mitosis. The sprouts soon open to form new alveoli, which in turn produce their new generations of alveoli, until they ultimately become so numerous as to meet their neighbors, and by mutual pressure to assume angular shapes and reduce the surrounding connective tissue to thin septa between the alveoli. These sprouts are denied by those who regard the alveoli as unlined tissue spaces; for them, all increase in the number of alveoli is due to the further septation of large cavities.

Shortly after birth the septa are so thin that the rich capillary network running through them is brought practically in contact with the alveolar walls on either side, and the oxygen–carbon dioxide exchange can take place on both sides of the flattened vascular plexus for more efficient breathing. The premature infant suffers from the fact that this normal relation of alveolar epithelium and capillary network has not yet been fully attained. Not only are the alveoli few but the smallness of their number permits wide septa between them, in which the capillary plexus may lie centrally, not near a surface. The oxygen–carbon dioxide exchange of breathing then takes place between air and tissue fluid, and only secondarily between tissue fluid and blood. The consequent partial retention of CO_2 may be the cause of the acidosis quite commonly encountered in these infants.

Three or four generations of thin-walled spaces, consisting of alveolar ducts, infundibular sacs, and alveoli, derived by branching from a single terminal bronchiole, constitute a respiratory unit of definite volume. Within this combined space the exchange of oxygen for carbon dioxide can take place to the maximum advantage, both as to thoroughness and as to time. To maintain this volume during the continued growth of new terminal branches from the tips of the latest alveoli, the proximal air sacs of the units are at the same time converted into bronchioles that serve merely as passages for the air to and from the units. This is accomplished by the progressive downgrowth onto the alveolar duct of the bronchial musculature, which constricts the lumen and separates the surrounding capillary plexus from the epithelium. The irregular air space becomes narrow and tubular, and the alveoli studding its walls, since they are no longer able to function, shrink and form part of the duct wall, assuming cuboidal epithelium. Thus as new sprouts grow from the alveoli, new bronchioles are added to the parental tree. The newer bronchioles are the so-called "respiratory bronchioles," distinguished by having occasional degenerate alveoli along their walls as proof that they were derived from former alveolar sacs or infundibula (Fig. 20). From the sixth fetal month new alveoli and new bronchioles continue to be added as long as the growth of the individual persists. In the lung of the aged, respiratory bronchioles may not exist, the jutting alveoli having ultimately all been absorbed into the bronchiolar wall. The change in the contents of the alveoli at birth from amniotic fluid to air causes no break in this growth. The lung of an adult is larger than that of an infant not because the units and alveoli are larger, but because there are more units and more alveoli. The alveolus of the infant is normally of the same diameter as that of the adult; the number of generations of bronchial branches, however, has increased from about 20 to some 30 or more.

The continuing growth of new alveoli in childhood is an important factor in recovery after lobectomy.[19] Immediately after the operation the remaining lung tissue expands rapidly in an attempt to fill the vacant space, and does so by an increase in alveolar size. In this condition the optimal ratio between the volume of alveolar air and its active air surface in intimate relation with blood capillaries is lost and the efficiency of the lung is thereby damaged. In the adult, with the loss of growth power, this condition must persist; * in the child, on the other hand, lung growth soon accelerates,

* Recent attempts to wall off the now vacant portion of the pleural cavity from which the diseased lobe has been removed and thus prevent overexpansion of the remaining lobe or lobes are described by L. A. Brewer, A. F. Bai, and W. M. G. Jones, "The development of the pleural partition to prevent overexpansion of the lung following partial pulmonary resection," *J. Thoracic Surg. 31,* 165–182 (1956).

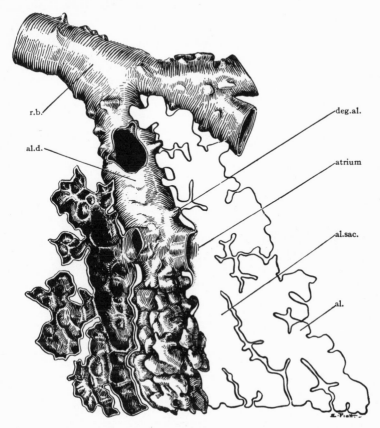

Fig. 20. Lobule of lung, based on reconstructions of lung of kitten: *al*, alveolus; *al.d*, alveolar duct; *deg.al*, degenerating alveolus; *r.b*, respiratory bronchiole. [From J. L. Bremer and H. L. Weatherford, *Textbook of histology* (Blakiston Div., McGraw-Hill, New York, ed. 6, 1944).]

new alveoli of normal size replace their emphysematous forebears, new branches are added to the bronchial tree, and the enlarged remaining lobes become normal and continue their normal growth (Fig. 21).

Within the lung proper the chief anomalies are faulty or abnormal lobation and bronchiectasis.[20] The first is easily understandable as due to the absence of certain secondary bronchi, to their increased number, or to irregularities in their arrangement. Bronchiectasis may appear in either the cylindrical or the sacular form. The former is the result of the premature local cessation of growth

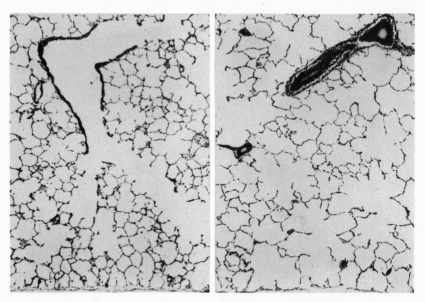

Fig. 21. Similar sections of remaining lung of kitten (*left*) and of adult cat (*right*) 1 month after lobectomy on the same side; same magnification. The alveoli of the kitten are of normal size, those of the cat are abnormally expanded. [From J. L. Bremer, *J. Thoracic Surg.* 6, 339 (1937).]

in a certain portion of the bronchial tree, as shown by the failure to produce new alveoli. Since alveolar development normally extends from the sixth fetal month to the end of childhood, this type of bronchiectasis may be either congenital or of postnatal origin, for development does not cease with birth. Without alveolar sprouts the affected air passages become swollen, flaccid blind tubes, lacking both the ciliated epithelium and the musculature and cartilage plates of active bronchioles, and hence peculiarly liable to infection (Fig. 22).

Attention has been called to the high percentage of cases in which congenital bronchiectasis accompanies situs inversus of the viscera and especially dextrocardia.[21] There seems to be no developmental basis for this coincidence except the fact that embryonic anomalies, indicating an imperfect ovum, are apt to be multiple. The syndrome of dextrocardia, bronchiectasis, and sinusitis is sufficiently well recognized to be given a name (Kartagener's triad).

Some bronchiectatic cysts may be due to similar causes. The cysts are characteristically in the upper lobes, the bronchiectatic

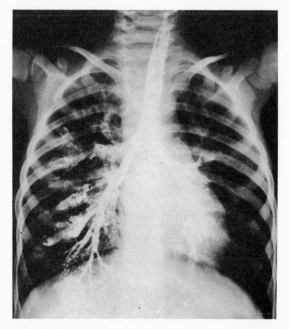

Fig. 22. Bronchiectasis as shown by roentgenogram (Neuhauser).

tubules in the lower, and it has been suggested that gravity alone may influence their shape. The majority of cysts, however, occur not at the end, but along the course, of some branch of the bronchial tree, with inlet proximally and perhaps several outlets, and are probably caused by some valve action or obstruction on the proximal side. In the presence of a valve or veil within a given bronchus,[22, 23] the immediately distal portion of the same bronchus might expand from the pressure of the entrapped air. This suggestion is supported by the fact that comparable veils or valves are known in other parts of the air passages, one type of which has already been mentioned (p. 12) as occasionally developing within the nasal passages from normal epithelial plugs, which may rarely persist and organize. Similar valves or veils are sometimes present within the trachea at birth, and call for surgical interference.

The *blood supply* of the early embryonic lung is unusual. The walls of the foregut are supplied by capillaries derived from the originally plexiform paired dorsal aortae (p. 126) draining into the systemic veins of the body wall, and as the lung bud develops from the foregut it also is surrounded by a special portion of this splanchnic plexus, which may be considered the primary pulmonary circulation. But before the arterial and venous roots of this net have become definitely established, the paired pulmonary arteries from the ventral aorta (p. 171) grow caudally at a rapid rate, preceded by their common prepharyngeal capillary plexus, which finally meets and joins with the splanchnic plexus by the anastomosis of the component capillaries. Meanwhile, the normal lengthening of the pharynx has brought the lung bud to the level of the cardiac atrium, which responds to the propinquity of the capillary plexus surrounding the bud by sending out a vascular sprout to tap it and thus become the originally single pulmonary vein (Fig. 67, *I*). Rarely, this normal condition may be disturbed. If the pharynx lengthens so slowly that the atrium has already assumed its muscular coat before the lung bud, with its vascular plexus, has reached the atrial level, no pulmonary atrial venous sprout will be formed (Fig. 23, *A*), for only when uncoated can endothelium produce new branches. With further growth of the pharynx the lung may receive a sprout from the venous sinus (Fig. 23, *B*) or from one of its component branches. In either case the lungs will receive both systemic and pulmonary arteries, but drain only into the systemic venous system. The various veins serving for this anomalous pulmonary drainage to the right side of the heart are listed by Johnson;[24] the superior vena cava and the innominate vein are the most common, and less frequent are the inferior vena cava, the azygos vein, the left subclavian vein, the coronary sinus, the portal vein, and even the lymphatic duct. In all such cases there is a right heart enlargement. The frequency of this condition has been called to the attention of pathologists by the current use of cardiac catherization.

The pulmonary plexus is thus normally common to two sets of vessels, the bronchial and the pulmonary. As the bronchi lengthen and the lung parenchyma develops, the common plexus generally divides. The bronchial vessels annex the portions supplying the muscles and the other mesenchymal structures, the septa and the visceral pleura; the pulmonary vessels take over the parts surrounding the alveoli and the alveolar sacs. Many connections remain between the two portions, and during the growth period, as new alveolar units develop and the older units are added to the bron-

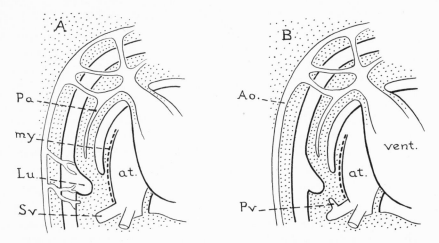

Fig. 23. Diagrams showing varying relations of lung bud to atrium of heart, and their effect on the origin of the pulmonary vein. Compare with Fig. 67, I. Explained in text. Ao, aorta; at, atrium; Lu, lung; my, myocardium; Pa, pulmonary artery; Pv, pulmonary vein; Sv, sinus vensosus; vent, ventricle.

chial tree (p. 37), constant rearrangement of the plexus is necessary. Even in the adult a few such connections between the two divisions of the original plexus may be found, often of greater than capillary size. This union of the two vascular systems, pulmonary and systemic, offers opportuniy for many types of abnormal drainage. One lung or one lobe may lack its proper pulmonary venous branch, either by agenesis or by later thrombosis, and make use of these connections to transfer the venous drainage of the alveoli to the systemic veins. In one instance,[25] when the left atrium was blocked by early mitral stenosis and closure of the foramen ovale, the pressure from three of the pulmonary veins caused a reversal of flow in the fourth, which, through enlargement of certain elements of the capillary plexus and use of the bronchial veins, supplied the drainage for the three remaining lobes to the systemic veins. Other variations of the pulmonary veins entail concomitant changes in the heart and will be mentioned in the description of that organ (p. 147).

Agenesis of one pulmonary artery, usually that to the right lung, has been noted in a few cases.[26] The affected lung receives its sole blood supply from the bronchial system. Until birth the lung grows as usual, but postnatally, since the oxygen exchange is minimal, it remains small and atelectatic; the contralateral lung is correspondingly enlarged to do full duty for both. On the other hand, an accessory artery,[27] from the lower thoracic or upper lumbar aorta, may pass through the pulmonary ligament to supply the posterior basal sector of the lung, either in addition to the normal branch of the pulmonary artery to that portion or replacing that vessel, which then degenerates. In the latter case, the affected lobule, since it is supplied only by arterial blood, remains after birth as a sequestered or ectopic fetal lobule, its original bronchus ending blindly. In this form it may become cystic or inflamed, and in the latter case may adhere to the pariental pleura and in this way receive an additional or replacing artery from any portion of the chest wall, and probably also venous drainage through some systemic vein. Whether with the normal pulmonary or with the abnormal systemic blood supply, the lung shows occasional arteriovenous anastomoses (A-V shunts), usually at the bronchiolar level.

Perhaps the most bizarre of the anomalies derived from the participation of the pulmonary arteries in the splanchnic plexus is shown in those very rare cases in which the left pulmonary artery passes to the right of the trachea and either behind or in front of the oesophagus on its way to the left lung. The right pulmonary artery and the ligamentune arteriosum are in their normal positions. In all probability this course of the left artery represents the use and enlargement of certain right-sided portions of the common systemic and pulmonary arterial plexus surrounding the foregut, and the obliteration of the corresponding normal left portions. A similar use of the foregut plexus is postulated to explain certain uncommon courses of the right subclavian artery (p. 179). The making of a new arterial pathway through a three-dimensional capillary plexus is readily accomplished in the young embryo, when many future arteries are still merely endothelial tubes without fibrous or muscular coats. The spread of the outer layers along such an enlarged vessel cuts off many of its former plexus connections and thus isolates it, without injury to the plexus itself. Perhaps the ultimate cause of the new course of the left pulmonary artery may be traced to some chance twist of the young embryo at a certain level and at a critical time.

4 ⎯⎯⎯

INTESTINAL TRACT

The foregut and hindgut are simple pockets of the entodermal yolk sac drawn into the head fold and tail fold, respectively, as the embryo lengthens (Fig. 24, *A, B*). With continued
growth of the embryo the fore- and hindguts become long slender
tubes, while the upper portion of the yolk sac from which they
spring is relatively reduced in diameter until it becomes the tubular
vitelline duct in the yolk stalk (*C*) connecting the mid-portion of
the gut with the small rounded yolk sac lying on the placenta. Thus
the early gut appears as a continuous tube from mouth to anus,
with a branch running out in the umbilical cord to the yolk sac.
The cranial part of this tube, the pharynx, has already been
described, as well as the subdivision of the caudal end of the single
foregut into two parallel tubes, the trachea serving the lungs and
the oesophagus forming an integral part of the intestinal tract
(p. 29). At the caudal end of the embryo also a somewhat similarly
expanded portion of the hindgut, called the cloaca (*C*), is divided
into the tubular rectum dorsally, continuing the intestinal tract to
the anus, and ventrally the urogenital sinus (*D*), which, as the
name implies, is to supply portions of the urinary and genital tracts,
to be studied later (p. 86). These two subdivisions of the tract
occur quite early in development; in the 6-week embryo (10–20
mm) the intestinal tract is a continuous tube from pharynx to anus,
with the exception of two local enlargements, one in the foregut
for the future stomach and one along the course of the hindgut for
the caecum.

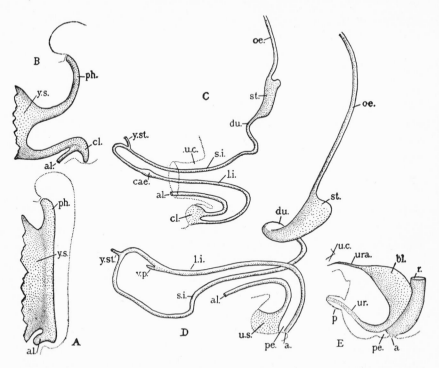

Fig. 24. Stages in the development of the digestive tube: (A) rabbit of 9 days; (B) man, 2.15 mm (after His); (C) pig, 12 mm; (D) man, 17.8 mm (after Thyng); (E) man, 5 months. *a*, anus; *al*, allantois; *bl*, bladder; *cae*, caecum; *cl*, cloaca; *du*, duodenum; *l.i.*, large intestine; *oe*, oesophagus; *p*, penis; *pe*, perineum; *ph*, pharynx (foregut); *r*, rectum; *s.i.*, small intestine; *st*, stomach; *u.c.*, umbilical cord; *ur*, urethra; *ura*, urachus; *u.s.*, urogenital sinus; *v.p.*, vermiform process; *y.s.*, yolk sac; *y.st.*, yolk stalk. [From J. L. Bremer and H. L. Weatherford, *Textbook of histology* (Blakiston Div., McGraw-Hill, New York, ed. 6, 1944).]

The stomach soon bulges dorsally, and the overgrowth of its dorsal wall, the greater curvature, produces a bend in the tube, with the result that at its lower outlet the stomach points at first ventrally or even cranially (Fig. 24, *C, D*), and this in turn induces a reverse bend in the duodenum directly below. To save space between the back and the abdominal wall, the greater curvature of the stomach soon rotates to the left (slightly displacing the oesophagus to the same side), the duodenal bend to the right. In the caecum, though it is at first a symmetrical swelling (*C*), the entire overgrowth is soon located on the antimesenteric border, causing a deep unilateral pouch, the ileal end of which is bent so sharply that the ileum now enters at right angles to the colon. The appendix is a secondary outgrowth.

In the early embryo, the increase in length of the intestinal tract keeps pace with the growth of the embryo; but soon, in order to provide the requisite surface area (internal) for the ultimately huge number of active epithelial cells necessary for the proper disposal of ingested food while at the same time retaining its tubular form, the tract must grow rapidly. This lengthening can be accomplished only by the bending or coiling of the tube, and to permit this action, while at the same time preserving the vascular and nervous supply, the various mesenteries are provided. The dorsal wall of the earliest tubular intestinal tract lies at first close against the notochord, in the mid-line. The aortae are then paired and run just laterally. With the development of the vertebral bodies and the union of the two aortae the intestinal tract lies ventral to the single aorta, and with the encroachment of the intraembryonic coelom from both sides, aided perhaps by some pull of the yolk sac, the tissue between aorta and gut wall, from the oesophagus cranially to the cloaca caudally, spreads out as a thin sheet, the mesentery, which thus consists of two layers of peritoneum, connecting the parietal peritoneum of the dorsal wall of the peritoneal cavity with the visceral peritoneum covering the gut. In the abdominal region the two halves of the intraembryonic coelom are continuous with each other around the ventral side of the gut tube and therefore the intestine is attached only by a dorsal mesentery. In the thorax, however, the intraembryonic coelom sends two separate pockets forward, one on either side of the gut, which produce between them two mesenteries, a dorsal and a ventral. In the oesophageal region these two mesenteries are known as the mediastinum.

The dorsal mesentery of the stomach is the greater omentum; but the stomach develops in close relation with the dorsal edge of the septum transversum, which serves as an additional attachment or mesentery. After the growth and expansion of the liver within the septum (p. 71), the ventral mesentery of the stomach comprises the lesser omentum, the capsule of the liver, and the falciform ligament, all derived from the original septum. The two ends of the gut tube, down to the outgrowth of the hepatic duct cranially, and the whole cloaca caudally, are thus held rigidly in position by their double attachment and can increase in length no faster than the surrounding structures. The middle portion, lacking the ventral mesentery, can by looping and coiling accommodate a much greater length within the restricted space.

The first result of the lengthening of this middle portion of the intestine is the formation of a ventrally directed loop, connected with the yolk sac by the short yolk stalk, and extending out into the umbilical coelom, because the intraembryonic part of that cavity is mostly filled at this time by the greatly enlarged liver (Fig. 24, C). At first the loop is simple and in the sagittal plane, and the limb on which the caecal swelling is soon to appear (and therefore comprising both the distal ileum and the proximal section of the colon), lies in the caudal position. At about seven weeks the cranial limb of the loop (i.e., most of the small intestine) begins to coil, further lengthening of the intestine being largely limited to this portion. The tight coils soon fill most of the available space (Fig. 25, a). The colon makes no tight coils, but its slower growth is accommodated by a dextral rotation of the whole primary loop on its own axis through more than a half-turn; this brings the caecum and proximal colon first to the cranial side and then to the right side of the base of the loop, while the caudal half of the colon swings correspondingly to the left. This condition continues until the end of the tenth week, when the coiled intestines are normally returned [1] to the abdominal cavity, space being provided partly by the reduced growth of the liver and the degeneration of the meso-nephroi (p. 88), partly by the coincident rapidly increased expansion of the body walls, an expansion which enlarges the cavity both in circumference and in linear extent. This can be seen by comparing drawings of embryos of appropriate ages; at 7 weeks, while the intestines are still in the umbilical coelom, the phallus practically touches the caudal wall of the umbilical cord (Fig. 25, a), while at 9 weeks or the time of their return to the true abdominal cavity, these two structures are separated by a considerable extent of newly formed abdominal wall (b). When all the intestinal coils are returned to their permanent location, the coelom in the umbilical cord is normally obliterated.

Certain anomalies are to be expected from this extra-abdominal position of the intestines. Omphalocele or umbilical hernia, denot-

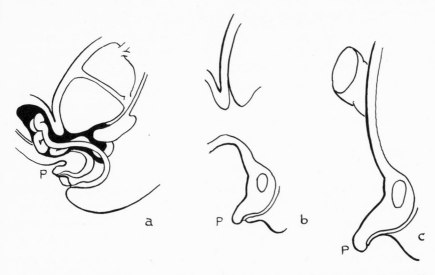

Fig. 25. (a) Embryo of 23 mm (Cullen), intestinal coils in umbilical coelom; note absence of abdominal wall below umbilical cord. (b) 45 mm; (c) 52 mm, coils withdrawn; increasing vertical length of wall.

ing the presence at birth of coils of intestine within the expanded proximal coelom of the umbilical cord, is due to delayed withdrawal of the coils. The fault here seems to lie in the retarded development of the body wall, for portions of the liver may be included in the sac (Fig. 26) along with the other upper abdominal viscera—transverse colon, pancreas, portions of the stomach, even spleen—forced out by the small size of the true abdominal cavity. This protrusion of the viscera into the persisting umbilical coelom should be sharply distinguished from gastroschisis or visceral ectopia, in which there is partial absence of ventral abdominal wall at some point other than the umbilicus. In explanation for the local delay in body-wall growth, one might note that the materials for the parietal and ventral muscles and fasciae (and for the bones in the chest wall) originate in the somites and grow forward on both sides to the midventral line. This growth is readily disturbed. In chick embryos it has been found that even slight injuries to the early somites may result in partial absence of the ventral wall at corresponding levels,[2] with eventration of abdominal viscera and even ectopia cordis.

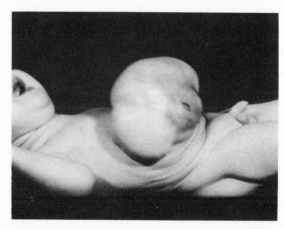

Fig. 26. Omphalocele in boy of 4 months, containing almost half of the abdominal viscera. [From W. E. Ladd and R. E. Gross, *Abdominal surgery in infancy and childhood* (Saunders, Philadelphia, 1941).]

In gastroschisis the cleft in the body wall is at some point lateral to the linea alba. This condition may be the result of the local cessation of growth of the wall tissue representing one or more somites, the gap thus formed being then bridged over by tissue from the neighboring somites above and below; the small defect in the embryonic body wall would become, with the later vertical wall growth, a longitudinal cleft in the older fetus. It has also been suggested that the longitudinally disposed abdominal muscles may arise directly from the mesenchyma of the umbilical cord [3] or from that of the dermatome of the somites, whereas the lateral and oblique muscles are derived from the myotome proper, which thus expands only to the linea semilunaris. Such a difference in origin may lead to failure of the two groups of muscles to meet and offer another explanation for the condition found in gastroschisis.

Midgut. It is customary among surgeons to designate as midgut that portion of the intra-abdominal intestinal tract supplied by the superior mesenteric artery, while the inferior mesenteric artery serves the hindgut, and branches from the coeliac axis and from the various thoracic arteries supply the foregut. Embryologically there is no justification for this use of these terms. The midgut includes strictly only that part of the intestinal tract in intimate relation with the yolk sac, from which the fore- and hindguts grew, or with its derivative, the yolk stalk. As such it is represented at birth only by the root of Meckel's diverticulum, if this is present, and, if the yolk stalk has been entirely obliterated, no midgut can be said to exist. Yet with this in mind the surgical nomenclature is frequently of real value, and the term midgut especially, as indicating the freely movable small intestine (with the addition of the adjacent colon as far as the mid-line), should certainly be retained.

Meckel's diverticulum. Even without umbilical hernia the retracting intestine may remain attached to the umbilicus by an abnormally persistent yolk stalk. This condition was well described by Meckel in 1815, and the stalk has since been called by his name. It is fairly common at birth, and although it may remain throughout life and cause no symptoms, yet it must always be considered a potential source of danger. It appears in several forms. The stalk may be patent and continuous throughout, opening to the surface as an umbilical fistula, delivering fecal matter; it may be patent at both ends, with a fibrous cord between, and the outer end may either open to the surface and produce a glairy secretion of its own cells (umbilical sinus) or be closed as a cyst. In either of the two last cases, blood is supplied by terminal branches of the intestinal vessels running in the fibrous cord. The most usual form of the diverticulum is as a blind branch of the ileum 1½ to 3 ft above the caecum, either attached to the umbilical scar by a fibrous cord or hanging free in the abdominal cavity. The free end may secondarily become adherent to some other point in the abdominal cavity. The branch is lined by ileal mucosa and is in every way like a portion of the bowel which it joins, except for the presence in about 60 percent of the cases of areas of gastric mucosa, a characteristic shared by other blind branches (duplications) of the bowel. It may also show a cluster of pancreatic cells, representing an accessory pancreas.

The symptoms caused by the presence of Meckel's diverticulum vary with its type. As a fistula it is readily recognized. When attached to the belly wall it may cause angulation of the ileum, with resultant partial or complete obstruction; when floating free in the cavity it may become inflamed, closely simulating appendicitis, or it may invert itself into the lumen of the bowel, thereby serving as the advancing point of an intussusception. Lastly, and because of the aberrant gastric mucosa, it may give symptoms of ulceration, with hemorrhage or even perforation.

Even when no portion of Meckel's diverticulum remains, one of its accompanying blood vessels may be a source of danger. The yolk sac is supplied through the yolk stalk by an end branch of the superior mesenteric artery, representing the originally multiple paired vitelline arteries. The vein draining the yolk sac, on the other hand, passes to the base of the mesentery or even to the porta of the liver, at a higher level, and only secondarily supplies the intestinal loop by a branch, the superior mesenteric vein, while the main trunk, the single remaining vitelline vein, traverses the coelomic cavity in a separate sheath of mesenteric tissue (Fig. 27, *a*). With the disuse of the yolk sac and the loss of the diverticulum, the vitelline artery normally is lost, but it may remain, either patent and supplying an umbilical sinus (*b*) or as a fibrous cord. The vein also commonly disappears, but may persist as a cord, and by its connection with the base of the mesentery or the hepatic porta is readily differentiated from the fibrous phase of Meckel's diverticulum, though equally liable to cause intestinal angulation (*c*).

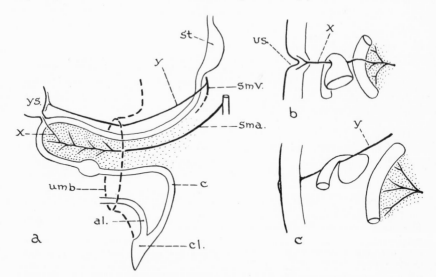

Fig. 27. Diagrams to show (a) the position of the vitelline artery x and vein y, and the possible dangers in case of their abnormal retention (b) and (c). *al*, allantois; *c*, colon; *cl*, cloaca; *sma, smv*, superior mesenteric artery, vein; *st*, stomach; *umb*, umbilicus; *us*, umbilical sinus; *ys*, yolk sac.

In returning to the abdominal cavity the intestines retain the same relative positions that they held in the umbilical coelom (Fig. 28). The caecum and proximal colon lie to the right, and come to rest on the right dorsal peritoneal wall; the distal colon rests on the

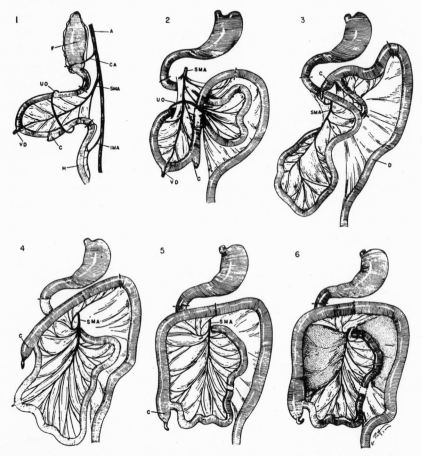

Fig. 28. Schematic drawing of normal development, rotation, and attachment of the midgut. The midgut in each sketch lies between the dotted cross lines and represents that portion of the alimentary tract from duodenum to mid-transverse colon which is supplied by the superior mesenteric artery. (1) fifth week, lateral view; (2) tenth week, frontal view; (3) early in eleventh week; (4) late in eleventh week; (5) late fetal life, rotation is complete with caecum in normal position; (6) final stage, attached mesenteries indicated by stippling. A, aorta; C, caecum; CA, coeliac axis; D, descending colon; F, foregut; H, hindgut; IMA, inferior mesenteric artery; SMA, superior mesenteric artery; UO, umbilical orifice; VD, vitilline duct, in yolk stalk. [From W. E. Ladd and R. E. Gross, *Abdominal surgery in infancy and childhood* (Saunders, Philadelphia, 1941).]

left wall, and the transverse portion joining these two crosses the mid-line cranial to the duodenum and to the superior mesenteric artery. The proximal and distal, or ascending and descending, colons then become fixed by the fusion of their mesenteries with the dorsal peritoneum, while the mesentery of the transverse colon is held by its base only, and this portion of the gut is thus more movable. It not infrequently happens, however, that this normal pattern has not been attained at birth. The caecum may lie in the upper right quadrant (Fig. 29) or under the ensiform cartilage, or even on the left side. Such abnormal conditions seem to indicate that the whole colon had lengthened too slowly, and that consequently the primarily caudal limb of the original midgut loop was composed chiefly of ileum, with very little colon. The malpositions may persist because of the formation of adhesions, but they are usually soon corrected by the continued lengthening of the proximal colon and the shifting of the caecum to a more normal site.

During the formation of these various loops and rotations of the intestinal tract the dorsal mesentery must be greatly affected. By the rotation of the greater curvature of the stomach to the left, the curved first portion of the duodenum is carried to the right dorsal wall of the abdominal cavity and there firmly fastened by

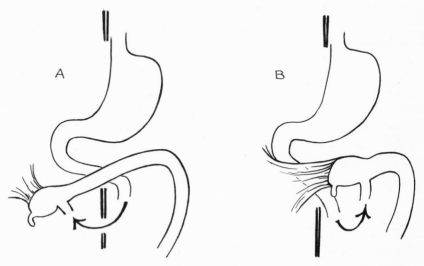

Fig. 29. The position of the caecum or of its attachment low in the upper right quadrant compresses the duodenum against the vertebral column.

the fusion of its mesentery to the parietal peritoneum. Its transverse portion, similarly fixed, extends across the midline. In the formation of the midgut loop and the rapid lengthening of its component sections of intestine a relatively constricted mesenteric base is thus provided for a large area of distribution, and the later rotation of the loop twists this base or pedicle and reduces its linear extent still further. In conditions providing insufficient mesenteric base for a considerable extent of intestines, whether in the simple loop of the embryo or in malposition of the caecum in the infant, there is always danger of volvulus, the twisting of a section of the intestine upon itself so as to occlude the lumen or interfere with the blood supply. From such a fate the midgut loop is normally saved by the reëstablishment of a broader base between two already fixed points, the duodeno-jejunal junction and the caecum, and along this diagonal line the mesentery of the jejunum and ileum adheres to the dorsal wall. In the case of persistent malposition of the caecum, however, where this line cannot be established, volvulus is always a real hazard.

Absence of sufficient adhesion of the mesentery of the transverse colon may result in a long loop of this portion of the colon, sometimes reaching to the pelvis. This is to be distinguished from congenital megacolon (Hirschsprung's disease), in which the colon is of enormous diameter. This latter condition is due to no intrinsic maldevelopment or disease of the colon itself, but to the malfunction or stenosis of the rectum or rectosigmoid below, resulting in immobility of that section and chronic obstruction of the colon above.[4]

Intrinsic anomalies of the intestinal tract. Diverticula and duplications of the intestinal tract [5]—the latter also known as ileum duplex, giant diverticula, enteric or enterogenic cysts—may occur anywhere along its length, but are most common in the ileum and duodenum. Meckel's diverticulum has been described, and by its origin from the yolk stalk is set off from this other group. The true diverticula may also be distinguished from the duplications by their method of growth. Diverticula develop as minute hollow buds from the epithelial lining of the gut into the subepithelial connective tissue or submucosa (Fig. 30, *a, b*) chiefly on the antimesenteric surfaces, in embryos of 20 to 30 mm (end of the second month).[6]

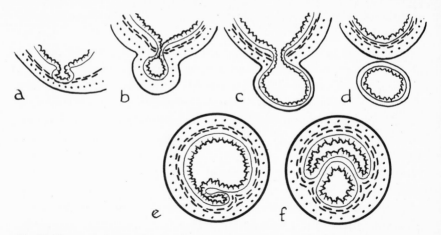

Fig. 30. Diagrams showing the development (a–d) of a thin-walled intestinal diverticulum or cyst and (e,f) of an intraluminal cyst. Circular musculature indicated by short lines, longitudinal muscles by dots.

The layers of the intestinal wall are well established by this time. The buds normally soon disappear as the intestine enlarges, but occasionally one may persist, force its way between bundles of the inner circular muscles, lift the weaker longitudinal layer or pass through it, and expand outside the intestine either as a diverticulum with a narrow pedicle or as a free cyst (c, d). The wall is composed of mucosa and serosa only, or with a few scattered strands of longitudinal muscle fibers. On the other hand, if no passage is found through the circular muscle layer, the diverticulum may expand within the submucosa lifting the mucosa above it as an intraintestinal cyst, or may burrow through the submucosa for some distance and then expand terminally into the parent lumen. Whether as terminal expansion or local cyst it may grow to such a size that the lumen of the intestine becomes entirely occluded (e, f). A similar terminally enlarged outgrowth of the trachea has already been described (p. 33).

The intestinal diverticula of embryonic origin are apt to be found singly and thus differ strikingly from those of postnatal and adult origin, known as acquired or pseudo diverticula, peculiar to the condition known as intestinal diverticulosis, the incidence of which increases with advancing years. In these also the lining mucosa pouches out through the other intestinal layers, often following the pathway of a penetrating artery or vein and hence seldom gathering any musculature of its own, and perhaps forming a terminal enlargement beyond the influence of peristaltic action where food may lodge and undergo bacterial fermentation.

The various diverticula just described are the only ones, always with the exception of Meckel's diverticulum, to which the name should be applied. Duplications of the intestine arise from a condition that is normal at 10–12 mm (about 6 weeks) and is primarily due to a phenomenon of embryonic growth incident to the rapid elongation of the intestine at that time. The acceleration of the growth rate of a tubular organ, whether local, as in the outgrowth of a new organ, or general, as in the lengthening of the intestine, is always initiated by the preliminary local multiplication of the epithelial cells, as though to provide a reserve that may be called upon to spread and line the extensive inner surface about to be provided. The mesenchymal tissues involved in the lengthening or outgrowth can apparently increase initially more rapidly than the epithelium. For instance, the future position of the outgrowth of the pancreatic duct is first indicated by a local mound of epithelial cells in the intestinal lining before any sign of the future bud appears externally. In the lengthening of a tubular organ such a local mound extends around the lumen as an internal ridge, and in the narrow embryonic intestine additions to the ridge soon lead to the occlusion of the lumen, known as the "epithelial plug" or solid stage. The solid stage never affects the whole intestinal tract at one time, but probably passes as a wave of solidification throughout its length. Certain regions may never be completely occluded (e.g., the oesophagus), retaining throughout a minute lumen enclosed within thick walls of massed epithelial cells. Normally the massed cells, whether of plug or of wall, secrete a fluid that soon gathers in small intercellular droplets, occupying vacuoles, which are frequently multiple and usually arranged in longitudinal rows or chains. By individual expansion the vacuoles coalesce, forming finally a new longitudinal channel. Meanwhile, the lengthening tube utilizes more and more of the massed cells until finally the main channel is lined only by the normal single layer. In rare cases an additional longitudinal chain of vacuoles may retain its individuality for a short distance and form an extra lumen.[7] This is the basis for all duplications, and even for triplications.[8] Such a condition is shown in Fig. 31 and the possible sequelae in the diagram (Fig. 32). The intestinal coats may grow between the two channels, first the submucosa, then the circular muscle layer, and the others in order. Most commonly the two tubes are united by their fused inner muscles, but the process may go on to a complete separation (Fig. 32, *f, g*).

One section of the intestinal tract, although occasionally producing duplications, has never been observed in such a solid stage. The lumen of the normal oesophagus [9] is always patent throughout, but the epithelial walls are sufficiently thick to allow within themselves the formation of vacuoles and accessory lumens (Fig. 31, *b, c*) and ultimate duplications.

The duplication is commonly on the mesenteric border, but may be in any other position. The twin lumens may communicate at one or more points, or there may be no communication. Perhaps the most usual arrangement is a single opening (Fig. 33), either at the oral or at the aboral end, and such duplications may continue

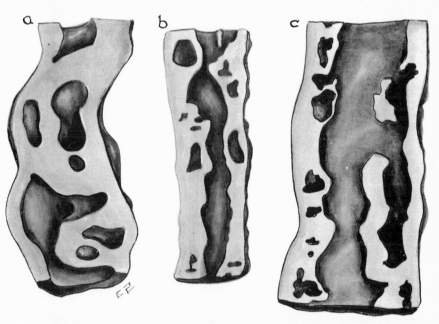

Fig. 31. Models (*a*) of the epithelium of the duodenum and (*b,c*) of the oesophagus, in human embryos of the seventh week (Johnson). The irregularly arranged vacuoles following the solid stage (*a*) may coalesce as a single lumen (*b*) or as a probable duplication (*c*).

their unfinished growth in length independently, without regard to the portion of intestine from which they are derived. The great majority of intestinal duplications remain within the abdominal cavity and receive their blood supply and nerves through the parent mesentery, but within the last few years three cases have been treated at this hospital in which a long duplication has invaded the chest.[10] Originating from either the jejunum or the duodenum, and passing through the diaphragm at the top of the lesser peritoneal cavity into the right pulmonary ligament, the duplication in all three cases remained extrapleural, but bulged into the pleural cavity sufficiently to embarrass the neighboring lung (Fig. 34). In two cases it reached the apex of the right pleural cavity; in one, after coiling in the right chest, the duplication traversed the mediastinum behind the oesophagus and aorta and appeared in the left chest, ending near the apex of the left pleural cavity. This whole journey above the diaphragm was made possible by the mesenchymal character of the tissues of the mediastinum and back wall at the time

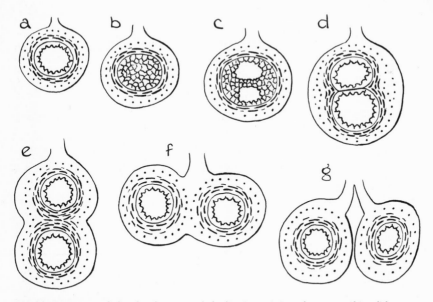

Fig. 32. Diagrams of the development of duplications: (a) early stage; (b) solid stage; (c) two vacuoles in cell mass; (d) two epithelial lumens, with conjoined basement membranes; (e) conjoined circular muscle layer between the lumens; (f) joined by serosa only; (g) free duplicate complete tubes. [From J. L. Bremer, Arch. Path. 38, 135 (1944).]

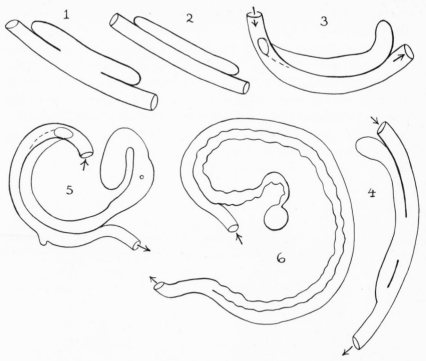

Fig. 33. Various more common types of intestinal duplications. Note bulbous ends of longer specimens. [From J. L. Bremer, *Arch. Path.* **38**, 136 (1944).]

when duplications may be developed. In the retropleural position the blood supply to these duplications is local.

The blind end, especially of a long duplication, is apt to be bulbous; perhaps it is molded by the force of the repeated waves of peristalsis or antiperistalsis, as the case may be. In this condition, although the tubular portion of the duplication copies the mucosa of the parent intestine, the bulb is lined, at least in part, by gastric mucosa. This juxtaposition of mucosal types often leads to the formation of ulcers at the outlet of the diverticulum, just as duodenal ulcers are formed at the outlet of the stomach; or "gastric" ulcers may form in the bulb itself. In other cases the duplication may develop as a separate entity, with no opening into the main lumen. Such an isolated duplication, if short, may become distended as a cyst, and, if still united to the intestine by interwoven muscles, the intracystic pressure may indent the common wall even to the extent of occluding the intestinal lumen as a form of extraintestinal occlusion.

The usual origin of the duplication from the mesenteric sector of the intestinal wall and its consequent location between the leaves of the mesentery which carries the vessels and nerves to the parent tube, as well as the frequent fusion of the musculature in the common wall, both point to the fact that simple removal of a duplication is as a rule contraindicated, and resection of both duplication and associated bowel, with anastomosis of the remaining ends, is commonly preferred.

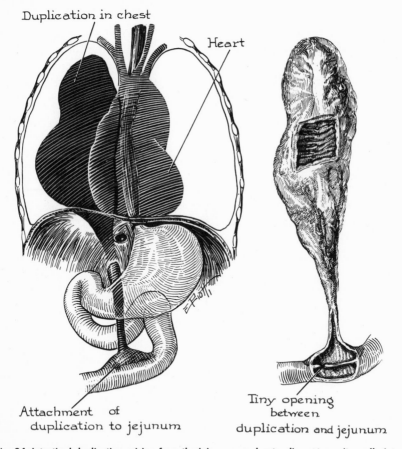

Duplication in chest

Heart

Attachment of duplication to jejunum

Tiny opening between duplication and jejunum

Fig. 34. Intestinal duplication arising from the jejeunum and extending retroperitoneally into the right chest. [From Gross et al., Ann. Surg. 131, 371 (1950).]

The dorsal intestinal fistula [11] is another type of apparent branch from the intestinal tract. The recognition of this anomaly as an entity rests upon a single published report,[12] appearing near the beginning of this century, describing the finding, in a 2-year-old girl, of a narrow tubular tract running dorsally from the rectum to open on the surface in the dorsal median line (Fig. 35, *a*), passing through a median defect in the fused bodies of the lower sacral vertebrae, between the nerve roots of the cauda equina, and through all the soft tissues of the back. Three somewhat similar cases had previously been reported, all in stillborn infants, in which the intestinal tract at various levels opened freely by large single or multiple mouths through the ventral plate of the still widely open medullary groove.[13] Still earlier, certain pioneer embryologists, by the artificially delayed insemination of the ova of fish [14] and of frogs,[15] had produced individuals in which, between the normal head end and tail end, a wide sagittal cleft separated the two halves of the body to expose the bulging upper surface of the yolk (Fig. 35, *b, c, d*).

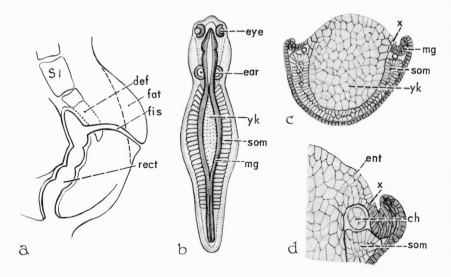

Fig. 35. (a) Dorsal intestinal fistula (after Keen and Coplin). (b) Anomalous pike embryo (Hertwig after Lereboullet). (c,d) Sections of anamalous frog embryos. *ch*, notochord; *ent*, entoderm; *def*, vertebral defect; *fis*, dorsal intestinal fistula; *mg*, medullary groove; *rect*, rectum; *som*, somite; *yk*, yolk; *x*, junction of ectoderm and entoderm. [From J. L. Bremer, *Arch. Path. 54*; 134 (1952).]

The open exposure of the yolk between the two body halves in the fish and frogs, the wide dorsal mouths of the intestines in the stillborn infants, and the neat tubular dorsal intestinal fistula probably represent three stages in the same process. In the attempt to repair the extreme damage, the two separated halves of the body, starting from both ends, would tend to grow together, reducing the cleft in both length and width and forcing the yolk mass to the new dorsal surface. In human embryos, with their minimal amount of yolk, the entodermal roof of the archenteron would be similarly forced dorsally by hydraulic pressure in the form of a tube or hollow longitudinal ridge between the two body halves (Fig. 36, *a*). At the surface the tube or ridge may remain closed or may rupture, its edges then fusing with the skin ectoderm (*b, c, d*).

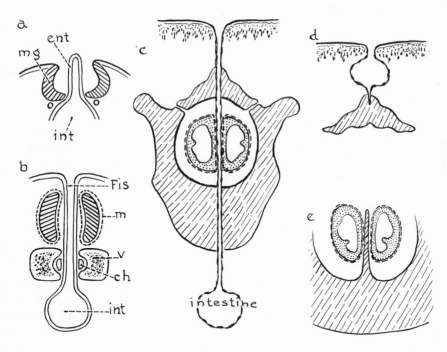

Fig. 36. Result of union of the two lateral halves of abnormal frog embryos; (*a*) hollow entodermal ridge rises between halves of medullary groove; (*b*) development of half vertebra and meninges; (*c*) complete fistula; (*d*) dorsal sinus; (*e*) bony spur from vertebral body. *ch*, notochord; *ent*, entoderm; *fis*, fistula; *int*, intestine; *m*, meninges; *mg*, medullary groove; *v*, vertebral half-body.

Like its ventral prototype, the umbilical fistula or patent form of Meckel's diverticulum, the dorsal fistula may disappear entirely, or may be reduced to a fibrous cord, perhaps with a closed cyst somewhere along its course, or a subcutaneous sinus, opening to the mid-line surface of the back by a pinpoint orifice (Fig. 36, *d*) and secreting drops of glairy fluid. This last variation closely resembles the umbilical sinus (p. 51). Meckel's diverticulum runs simply through the body cavity; the similar fistula to the back must pass through all the structures in the median line or between their respective halves if they remain apart, and even if it degenerates and disappears entirely during future growth it will leave a permanent record of its former presence in the more solid of the dorsal structures. In the vertebrae this is shown in three different forms; if the fistulous tract is lost soon after its formation, additional bone may fill the gap between the separated halves of the vertebral bodies, causing merely the increased breadth of the body or bodies; or if the fistula persists longer, the bodies of one or more vertebrae may develop around it, resulting in a circular or oval opening in the bone, or a longitudinal cleft through several vertebrae [16] which, on the later disappearance of the fistula, becomes an empty defect or hole through the vertebral body or bodies; or, perhaps in the case of a larger fistula, the two half-bodies may grow as individuals, each developing both right and left pedicular processes. In the last case, when the two bodies later come together the contiguous pedicular processes fuse to form a median spur, bony or cartilaginous, projecting into the spinal canal (Fig. 36, *e*). If any fragment of the fistulous tract remains (as, for instance, a fibrous cord attached to an inconspicuous mid-line skin dimple) it may enter the tip of this spur. Dorsally, the two meeting spinous processes may remain separate or fuse abnormally. In all three of these types of vertebral-body alteration—increased breadth, defect, or median ventral spur—the spinal canal will be locally widened. In the spinal cord, however, there is little attempt to close the cleft between the two separated halves. Perhaps they are restrained by the fixation of their nerve roots, ventral and dorsal. The ever-spreading mesenchyma grows between and around them and from it each half cord is enclosed by a meningeal investment, the two median walls of which meet in a fused layer of dura or arachnoid. In this fused layer any remnant of an earlier fistula, fibrous cord, or cyst may be found. Within this investment each half of the neural groove continues its normal development as best it can either as the lateral half (Fig. 36, c) of a spinal cord (diastematomyelia) or as one of a pair of malformed whole cords (diplomyelia),[17] each half attempting to complete the normal whole.

During the late fetal migration of the cord up the spinal canal, the injured cord segment may travel a considerable distance cranial to the injured bone, though both injuries were caused by the same fistulous tract. The widened cord may be but slightly compressed in the more cranial position, for the normal cord is loosely suspended, with plenty of unused space between it and the walls of the bony canal. The local absence, in diastematomyelia, of all spinal-cord commissures may pass unnoticed because of the abundant connections of the spinal nerves with others above and below the injury. The condition may remain hidden and unsuspected. Yet the presence of the bony injury alone is strong presumptive indication of the true condition.

In the presence of a bony spur long enough to become engaged between the leaves of the fused dural membranes or even to divide the vertebral canal locally into two compartments, full cranial migration of the cord is affectively prevented. The spur is found at the caudal end of the cleft in the cord, and the pressure it exerts on the commissures of the normal cord below the cleft is a measure of the tension of the cord above. The physical symptoms found in this type of diastematomyelia and their relief on removal of the spur are described by Ingraham and his group.[18] Perhaps this condition should be included with spina bifida and meningocele as possible causes of the Arnold-Chiari deformity, in which the medulla and cerebellum occupy the upper end of the spinal canal, as though they had been pulled down by the fixation or anchorage of the cord in its embryonic position as the spinal column grows longer. Others[19] point out that in the anchorage of the cord at the lower levels, and even in the normal cord with ventral flexion of the spine,[20] the stretching is absorbed in the cord itself, the upper nerve roots showing little or no angulation; the deformity is probably caused by the overgrowth of the brain.

If the fistula opens on the dorsal surface it usually passes through a rounded or oval accumulation of subcutaneous fat (Fig. 35, *a*) often bearing a conspicuous growth of hair, conditions also often found in relation with meningocele or other spinal-cord disorders, thus emphasizing the importance of the cord injury inherent in the fistula.

A few instances of dorsal intestinal fistula have been noted, although not as such, in the records of this hospital. One mother complained of the occasional fecal odor emanating from a tiny opening in her infant's skin in the upper lumbar region; this indicates a minute patent fistula perhaps furnished with a mucosal valve. In one infant the open outer end of the fistula was found near the dorsal mid-line in the lumbar region, and from it oozed a constant flow of nonfecal fluid, the product of its own epithelium. At operation a fibrous cord was found connecting it to the abnormally fused spinous process of a lumbar vertebra. In another case a large cyst, the lining of which resembled that of the fetal oesophagus, bulged from the dorsomedian wall into the right pleural cavity and was connected by a fibrous cord leading through a large median defect in the body of a lower thoracic vertebra to the median septum of a split spinal cord (diastematomyelia). In still another case, a median dorsal mound in the mid-thoracic region proved to be caused by a subcutaneous lobule of partially expanded lung, complete with atelectatic alveoli and a small bronchus leading to an underlying spinous process. Such a condition could well be the result of a former fistula from pharynx to surface at the level of the lung bud.

More recently, a large cyst was found in the cavity of the IV ventricle of the brain, with symptoms of pressure on the pons and medulla. At postmortem examination (during which any connections were destroyed) the lining epithelium was found to resemble in part that of the fetal pharynx, in part that of the fetal mouth, and therefore this cyst also may be, at least tentatively, included in this group. The dorsal intestinal fistula, in fragmented form, is apparently a not very uncommon finding.

Congenital atresias and stenoses of the intestine are characterized by the presence of a thin diaphragm across the lumen, complete in the case of atresia, and perforated in the case of stenosis. In all probability this diaphragm arises from the solid stage of the intestine, at a spot where secretion vacuoles fail to develop. Into the resulting solid mass of cells the submucosa from the sides of the gut, perhaps followed by some strands of circular muscle, grows in ring form (atresia). Tiny vacuoles developing in a longitudinal row through the solid mass would result in stenosis. In the rectum this intrinsic type of atresia must be distinguished from the complete interruption of the intestinal tract occasionally accompanying rectal fistula, and in the pyloris a stenosis may depend on the congenital hypertrophy of the muscular ring. In the oesophagus, since the solid stage does not normally exist, all atresias must be of the type following the formation of tracheo-oesophageal fistulae.

This simple explanation of the development of intestinal atresias and stenoses fits both conditions anatomically, but does not seem to agree with their distribution along the intestinal tract. The prolonged retention of the solid stage might be expected to occur in regions where longitudinal growth is slight, such as the oesophagus, the duodenum, and the rectum, all of which are so closely bound down to the underlying body wall that they can grow little if any faster than the body as a whole. Statistics show, however, that while the stenoses predominate in the duodenum, as might be expected, the atresias are more common in the upper ileum, a region of maximum lengthening, and individual instances of both types occur elsewhere along the full length of the bowel.[21] This difference in distribution of the two types is unexplained.

Mesenteric cysts. It will be obvious that isolated cysts in the mesentery may represent diverticula or duplications or dorsal fistulae. These can often be distinguished by the character of the wall, that of the cysts of diverticular origin being composed only of mucosa and serosa, or with a few scattered strands of smooth muscle, while if the cyst arose as a duplication the wall comprises all the layers of the intestine; an attached fibrous cord might indicate derivation from a dorsal fistula. Still another type may be encountered, the lymphogenous cyst, derived from an isolated portion of the mesenteric lymphatic plexus and readily distinguished by the characteristic endothelial lining.

The rectum is derived from the cloaca, the terminal expansion of the hindgut, the primarily caudal wall of which is formed by the cloacal membrane. The cloaca is in shape like a deep cup, laterally compressed to conform to the lineal cloacal membrane, and receiving, from above, the colon dorsally and the allantois ventrally; a short-lived tail gut leaves the distal dorsal angle.

Beginning at the fifth week the mammalian cloaca is gradually divided into the rectum dorsally and the urogenital sinus ventrally (Fig. 37), the latter so called because it is to form a part of the urinary bladder and most of the urethra, and is also to connect with the genital apparatus in both sexes. The common description of this division postulates the formation and descent of a crescent-shaped septum or fold, its origin not stated, cutting the cavity in the coronal plane from above downward. Actually the division of the cloaca, like that of the lower pharynx (p. 28), is due to the formation in the mesoderm of the lateral body walls of frontally disposed linear thickenings, with resulting internal ridges within the cloaca, which soon meet across the cavity and fuse, at first above and successively downward toward the cloacal plate. As the ridges meet, the opposing epithelial layers (entodermal) are obliterated, the mesenchyma is rearranged, and the single cloacal cavity is divided into the rectal tube dorsally and the urogenital sinus ventrally; by the continued extension of this fusion caudally the cloaca is completely divided, its entodermal lining obliterated where it is in contact with the encroaching mesoderm to form the perineum, and the cloacal plate reduced to the anal plate and the urogenital plate. The longitudinal ridges are thus often called the perineal ridges. The coelomic cavity follows caudally in the mesenchyma to produce the rectovesicle or rectovaginal pouch. Rectal fistulae represent persistent portions of the cloaca that have escaped obliteration as the result of the failure of some part of the ridges to meet and fuse. Following the downgrowth of a coronal septum or fold such a local escape seems impossible, but with the concept of two opposing lateral ridges, the meeting of which cuts the cavity in two like a pair of shears, it is readily seen that any notch or groove in either or both of the opposing surfaces may lead to a rectal fistula, the type depending on the position and direction of the groove. Rectovesical, rectourethral, and rectovaginal fistulae represent transverse grooves at various levels; rectoperineal fistulae indicate a diagonal groove, usually at a low level (Fig. 38). The fistula itself is a remaining portion of the original cloaca.

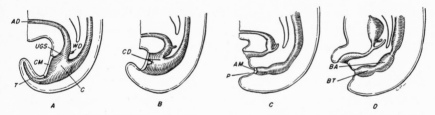

Fig. 37. Normal development of anus and rectum. (A) 7.5-mm embryo; (B) 9-mm; (C) 22-mm; (D) 42-mm. AD, allantoic duct; AM, anal membrane; BA, anal bulb; BT, terminal bulb; C, cloaca; CD, cloacal duct; CM, cloacal membrane; P, proctodeum; T, tail gut; UGS, urogenital sinus; WD, mesonephric (Wolffian) duct. [From W. E. Ladd and R. E. Gross, Abdominal surgery in infancy and childhood (Saunders, Philadelphia, 1941).]

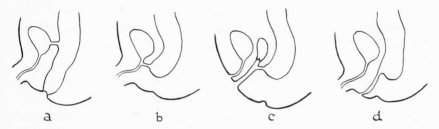

Fig. 38. Diagrams of fistulae: (a) rectovesicle; (b) rectourethral; (c) rectovaginal; (d) rectoperineal.

The fact that the most cranially situated rectovesical fistulae open slightly above the trigonal region of the bladder may help to settle the old embryological dispute, largely academic, as to how much of the bladder arises from the cloaca and how much from the allantois, which, after all, is a prolongation of the same cavity. The fistula, since it is the highest found of this type, probably represents the upper edge of the cloaca and hence marks its cranial extent. This indicates that most of the bladder comes from the expanded proximal end of the allantois. Beyond the bladder the allantois shrinks to a solid cord, the urachus, except in the rare cases in which it remains pervious to cause a urachal fistula.

The similarity in both cause and result of the rectal fistulae and the tracheo-oesophageal fistulae is obvious. In both instances a primarily single cavity is divided, completely in the case of the cloaca, incompletely in that of the lower pharynx (laryngopharyngeal junction), by the apposition of lateral internal ridges; grooves or irregularities in the opposing faces may permit portions of the original cavity to persist as fistulae. The direction of the division coincides with the direction of growth of the fore- and hindguts, cranially in the pharynx and caudally in the cloaca.

The rectum soon shows two consecutive fusiform widenings, the bulbus analis (rectal ampulla) and the bulbus terminalis, marked by three short constrictions of the tube, one above, one below, and a third between the two swellings. Various forms of stenosis or atresia recti may result from the partial or complete closure of these constrictions, while simple imperforate anus may be due either to the closure of the lowest constriction with resultant anal plug above the constrictor muscles or, if the tube is crossed merely by a thin veil, to the retention of the anal membrane, reinforced by the growth of fibrous tissue between its two layers. The rectum may be closed at the level of either the middle or the upper constriction, and may terminate at either point as a rectal pouch. The tube below, comprising one or both ampullae as the case may be, is ordinarily obliterated, the anal orifice absent; but as a variant the upper ampulla may be lost while the lower one, complete with anal orifice, is preserved. In all conditions the proctodaeum remains as a shallow surface dimple, and in many cases the blind rectal pouch is in connection by a fistula with some portion of the urogenital sinus or with the surface through the perineum.

5 ──────

LIVER AND PANCREAS

The liver first appears at the end of the fourth week as a ventral diverticulum of the foregut or pharynx, just at its junction with the cranial wall of the yolk stalk (Fig. 39, *A*). The diverticulum thus grows into the septum transversum, the shelf of mesenchyma forming the caudal wall of the pericardial cavity which is pierced by the proxminal ends of the vitelline veins on their way to the heart. The hepatic diverticulum soon sends out, from its cranial side only, several solid cords or sheets of cells.[1] The cords grow into the veins, pushing the endothelial walls before them, and at the same time the veins send out sprouts to meet them; the process combines invasion and concrescence. Since the cords produce branches that unite with each other in a close three-dimensional net, the veins become subdivided into many anastomosing channels, called sinusoids (Fig. 39, *B*).

Sinusoids[2] are vessels with definite characteristics. Their walls are as thin as those of capillaries, but their diameter is much greater. Since they occupy the space between rounded cords or tubules or sheets of cells, sinusoids are of irregular shape, not definitely tubular. Their endothelium is in close relation with the parenchyma, to which it is apposed with few or no connective-tissue cells between them. Capillaries, on the other hand, are commonly imbedded in connective tissue, although they occasionally come close to an epithelium (e.g., lung, glomerulus). Sinusoids are not connections between an artery and a vein, as are capillaries, but merely subdivisions of a vein along its course. Apparently the close apposition of the endothelium, on all sides, to the cells of the parenchyma,

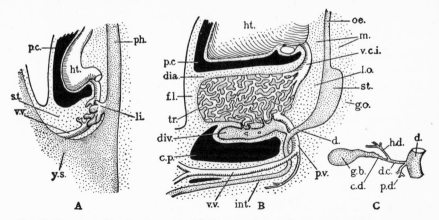

Fig. 39. Diagrams of the development of the liver: (A) human, fourth week; (B) pig, 6 weeks; (C) the ducts in a human adult. *c.d.,* cystic duct; *c.p.,* deritoneal cavity; *d.,* duodenum; *d.c.,* ductus choledochus; *dia.,* diaphragm; *div.,* diverticulum; *f.l.,* falciform ligament; *g.b.,* gall bladder; *g.o.,* greater omentum; *h.d.,* hepatic duct; *ht.,* heart; *int.,* intestine; *li.,* liver; *l.o.,* lesser omentum; *m,* mediastinum; *oe.,* oesophagus; *p.c.,* pericardial cavity; *p.d.,* pancreatic duct; *ph.,* pharynx; *p.v.,* portal vein; *s.t.,* septum transversum; *st.,* stomach; *tr.,* trabecula; *v.c.i.,* vena cava inferior; *v.v.,* vitelline vein; *y.s.,* yolk sac. [From J. L. Bremer and H. L. Weatherford, *Textbook of histology* (Blakiston Div., McGraw-Hill, ed. 6, 1944).]

and the retardation of the blood stream inherent in such a complicated venous net, are the most essential characteristics of these vessels, and must be of considerable physiological significance.

Normally all but one of the outgrowths from the diverticulum degenerate, leaving a single duct, the hepatic duct, to drain the entire mass of liver cords. This is possible because the cords form an anastomosing net, any member of which connects with all others. The diverticulum proper grows longer and its end becomes bulbous, so that it produces both the gall bladder and the cystic duct, and also at its proximal end becomes the common bile duct, into which both hepatic and cystic ducts drain (Fig. 39, *C*). The common bile duct may vary in length depending on which one of the row of the original multiple outgrowths is retained.

The mass of the liver, cords and sinusoids, divides the septum transversum into several layers. The thick upper layer becomes the tendinous centrum of the diaphragm. The middle portion supplies the scanty framework of reticular tissue that supports the cords and sinusoids. The lower layer forms the thin capsule of the liver and gall bladder. The falciform ligament, at first very broad with a mass of mesenchyma between its mesothelial surfaces, connects the liver with the ventral body wall while the duodenohepatic ligament runs dorsally to the duodenum. The location of the liver as the first organ encountered along the course of the food-bearing veins ensures its rapid growth in young embryos, and it responds by extending ventrally through the septum transversum toward the umbilical cord and dorsally as a right dorsal lobe (a similar left dorsal lobe is prevented at first by the presence of the stomach) which meets a narrow vertical ridge, the caval fold, projecting from the dorsal peritoneal wall, just to the right of the root of the mesentery. The fusion of fold and right dorsal lobe forms the right wall of the lesser peritoneal cavity (Fig. 40).

Veins of the liver. The sinusoids are derived from the vitelline veins, coming from the yolk sac on either side of the foregut. When the duodenum makes its abrupt ventral curve in response to the

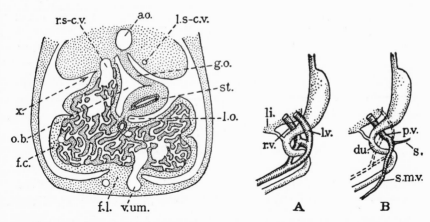

Fig. 40. Cross section of a mammalian embryo of 6 weeks, to show entrance into the liver of the left umbilical vein, v.um., through the falciform ligament, f.l., and of the right subcardinal vein, r.s-c.v., through the adhesion, x, between the right lobe and the dorsal wall. ao., aorta; f.c., fibrous capsule and serosa; g.o., greater omentum; l.o., lesser omentum; l.s-e.v., r.s-c.v., left, right subcardinal vein; o.b., omental bursa; st., stomach. [From J. L. Bremer, *Textbook of histology* (Blakiston, Philadelphia, ed. 5, 1936).]

Fig. 41. The formation of the portal vein, p.v., from parts of the two vitelline veins, r.v. and l.v. du., duodenum; li., liver; s., splenic vein; s.m.v., superior mesenteric vein. [From J. L. Bremer, *Textbook of histology* (Blakiston, Philadelphia, ed. 5, 1936).]

overgrowth of the greater curvature of the stomach, the two vitelline veins remain straight and fuse behind it; they have already fused in the front wall of the yolk stalk, and a third fusion is offered in the sinusoids. In this way the veins make two rings around the gut tube (Fig. 41, *A*). After the rotation of the stomach to the left and of the duodenum to the right, certain portions of the rings offer a straighter pathway and persist, and the rest degenerate and are lost. The result is a spiral relation of the now single vein and the duodenum (Fig. 41, *B*). The formation of these rings takes place with great regularity, only a very few variations from the normal having been reported.[3] Before its entrance into the liver the now single vitelline vein gives off the superior mesenteric and splenic veins, and from the entrance of the latter is known as the portal vein. Distal to the mesenteric branch it normally degenerates as the yolk sac shrinks (p. 52). Within the liver the portal vein loses its identity in the sinusoids, but becomes single again as the hepatic vein as it enters the heart.

From the placenta the paired umbilical veins pass through the umbilical cord to the body wall, and, in early embryos, run, one along each lateral body wall, to the level of the upper edge of the septum transversum. Here they meet and join the main trunks of the veins of the body wall, the paired common cardinal veins or ducts of Cuvier, and together as a single trunk on each side they turn mesially along this edge to join the vitelline veins as they enter the heart. The course of the umbilical veins is thus originally long and curved. When the expanding liver has reached the ventral wall, its sinusoids anastomose with branches of the left umbilical vein through the broad falciform ligament, and the umbilical blood uses and enlarges this new channel as a short-cut through the liver to the heart (Fig. 40). In the umbilical cord the two umbilical veins have already fused, and the right vein soon becomes obliterated, as well as the unused portion of the left vein in the body wall. In the liver the left umbilical vein establishes its own main channel among the sinusoids and runs along its under and dorsal sides to join the vitelline vein as it leaves the organ, connecting freely with the sinusoids, yet keeping open a main pathway on the under surface of the liver, known as the ductus venosus. The entrance to the ductus is guarded by a recently recognized sphincter [4] which may regulate the volume and pressure of the enclosed blood and determine the amount sent through the liver sinusoids.

This open passage may be a menace during birth and in the neonatal period, for through it debris from the placenta or from an unhealed umbilical scar may be carried to the lungs without entering the liver parenchyma. After birth the remains of the umbilical vein form the round ligament of the liver and the ligament of the ductus venosus.

The liver thus develops in intimate relation with the two large food-bearing veins of the body, the vitelline vein bringing food from the yolk sac (in the lower vertebrates, but a minimal amount in man) and the umbilical vein carrying both food and oxygen from the placenta in the higher vertebrates including man. Through its sinusoids it also plays a major role in the formation of the vena cava inferior, for the sinusoids of the right dorsal lobe anastomose in the caval fold with branches of the newly formed right subcardinal vein,[5] a derivative of the right posterior cardinal vein in the mesonephros (p. 89); by anastomosis with its fellow of the opposite side (the subcardinal anastomosis), and rearrangement of the cardinal veins, this new passage, greatly expanded, becomes the shortest route from the lower body and legs to the heart. As it enlarges it loses most of its sinusoidal connections and moves to the dorsal surface of the liver, and on its way to the heart it appropriates the channel of the original hepatic vein, the right and left branches of which now receive the name, and are said to empty into the vena cava inferior.

Anomalies of the liver. The liver thus plays a large part in the adult arrangement of the main veins of the body and, perhaps because of its importance in this respect, anomalies of this organ are very rare. In two or three cases the entire left lobe has been found absent,[6] and the main lobes may vary slightly in size or may be subdivided to form supernumerary lobes, but the two fusions of the liver sinusoids with veins of the ventral and dorsal body walls take place with great regularity. The most numerous anomalies of the liver are those of the ducts and of the gall bladder.[7] These structures, like the intestinal tract, pass through a solid stage (p. 59) preparatory to their normal elongation,[8] and, although the elongation of the ducts is far less extensive than that of the intestine, their lumen is correspondingly much narrower and is easily blocked by a small heap of epithelial cells. Here again numerous intercellular vacuoles are produced, which may become confluent in two or more channels and lead to duplication. The gall bladder itself may be lobed, bifid, or double (Fig. 42, *A, B*), and the cystic and common ducts may be double for a part or all of their length (*C, D*). The hepatic duct may also be double, but this may represent either a similar duplication or the retention of an extra member of the many original hepatic outgrowths from the diverticulum.

Very rarely one of these extra members of the original outgrowths may make a peculiar anastomosis. In a single case,[9] the most proximal outgrowth, nearest to the intestine, took no part in the formation of the liver but passed behind it in the loose mesenchyma of the septum transversum, and from there into the similar tissue of the lower mediastinum, just lateral to the oesophagus. Here it met and anastomosed with the tip of an accessory bronchus arising from the bronchial carina (p. 32), thus providing a continuous passage from the common bile duct to the trachea through which, after birth, both lungs were flooded with bile. On examination, the upper portion of the passage was found to have bronchial mucosa, musculature, and cartilage plates; the lower portion resembled the biliary tract. Actually the anastomosis is between an accessory bronchus and an accessory hepatic outgrowth, but perhaps the best term for the condition is "tracheobiliary fistula," or "tracheocholedochal tract."

The solid stage of the extrahepatic ducts, on the other hand, may result in their local atresia or obliteration (Fig. 42, *E, F, G*). Atresia of the cystic duct may produce enlargement of the gall bladder, often to great size. In the absence of bile the contents of the bladder consist of the secretion from the glands in the cystic mucosa, sometimes called "white bile." The occurrence of two bands of atresia in the common duct may also result in the expansion of the duct between them (*H*), also filled by local secretion. This type of cyst is to be distinguished from that caused by ideopathic dilatation of the common bile duct, in which the cyst connects freely with the cystic and hepatic ducts, and apparently through the proximal end of the duct with the duodenum, inasmuch as a probe can often be passed from the duodenum to the cyst. The closure that causes the dilatation may be due to some valve at the exit, or to spasm of the special muscles at the *papilla of Oddi*,[10] perhaps accompanied by an associated loss of tone of the intrinsic duct musculature. Naturally, any atresia of the common duct or hepatic duct, or any mechanism that prevents the entrance of bile into the intestinal tract, will produce jaundice.

The various cysts just described are all extrahepatic in that they are due to malformations of the extrahepatic ducts. Another group of congenital cysts is intrahepatic, and to understand this type some knowledge of the organogenesis of the liver is essential. The embryonic liver has already been described as a mass of branching and interconnecting solid cell cords or flat sheets of cells, derived by outgrowth from the cranial side of the original hepatic diverticulum, in the interstices of which lies a three-dimensional net of sinusoids. At about 6 weeks, short isolated lumens first appear in the solid cords, probably caused by the confluence of droplets of fluid secretion or excretion elaborated by the cells of the cord and discharged between them. The lumens are the bile capillaries, and at first are detached entities throughout the whole bulk of the liver. The tiny segments of lumen rapidly expand along the cords, meet each other, and join end to end, thus forming a complete network of bile capillaries, which then connects ultimately with the ducts

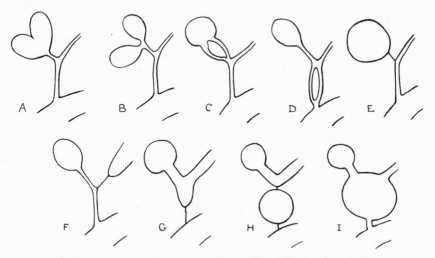

Fig. 42. Diagrams showing varieties of anomalies of the extrahepatic ducts.

leading to the hepatic diverticulum. The liver cells are still said to be arranged in cords or in sheets of conjoined cords, but actually the cords are like the tubules of other glands in that they contain a continuous lumen. If, at this early period of extension and anastomosis of the originally individual lumens, one or more of them fail to make the normal junctions with their neighbors and remain isolated, the pressure of the retained secretion soon causes that portion of the cord to swell in cyst formation, accompanied by a change of type of the enclosing epithelium. This is the probable mode of origin of the intraparenchymal type of congenital intrahepatic cyst, located within the liver lobules.

Intrahepatic cysts of a second type lie within the septa of the liver, between the liver lobules, and to understand their position and formation a knowledge of the development of the septa and lobules is necessary. The ingrowth into the liver of connective tissue derived from the hepatic capsule is a late phenomenon, occurring during the fourth and fifth months of intrauterine life. Before this time the cords and sinusoids form a homogeneous mass, in which run a few enlarged blood channels, without definite walls and opening on all sides into the sinussoidal plexus. The invading connective tissue entering at the porta accompanies and surrounds the main trunks and branches of the portal vein and of the intrahepatic ducts, enclosing these structures in a continuous sheath and thereby cutting off the many connecting lateral sinusoids and bile capillaries, and converting the former main channels through these two nets into an orderly system of coated veins and ducts. This does not destroy the usefulness of the severed sinusoids or cords, for through their connections with the remaining net they are still available for the circulation of blood or bile. A similar but less extensive connective-tissue invasion occurs at the cardiac end of the liver also, producing the hepatic veins and their branches. In the adult the mass of connective tissue surrounding a branch of the portal vein is called a portal canal and in this it is the rule to find a branch of the hepatic artery and two or more bile ducts, often interconnected around the vein. Rarely a chance growth of connective tissue may constrict a neighboring bile duct, causing its atresia,[11] or an intraseptal cyst may be formed between two points of constriction.

The liver till near birth is still an irregular network of veins and ducts, sinusoids, and liver cords, apparently without order, through which the columns of connective tissue, enclosing branches of the portal vein and of the intrahepatic ducts, make their way. (In the pig these columns are connected by sheets of fibrous tissue, which thus mark out primitive lobules, but in man only the cornerstones of such lobules are evident.) Rather suddenly the then terminal branches, still uncoated, of the two veins, portal and hepatic, inter-digitate and the sinusoids between them become arranged radially around the hepatic terminal twig, which now is known as the cen-tral vein and considered as the center of a lobule. The size of the lobule is determined by the physiologically optimal length of the sinusoids, that length in which the necessary interchanges between blood and tissue can best be completed. At birth the lobules are smaller than in the adult, not yet having determined the optimal length of liver cord, but with the taking of food this optimal length is soon established and the lobules throughout the liver become uniform in size. With further growth of the organ the lobules grow not in size but in number [12] by the simple branching of the central veins, the growth of the liver parenchyma, the rearrangement of the sinusoids, and the advancement of the connective tissue to enclose successive generations of portal twigs and bile ducts. Regen-eration of the liver after loss of a portion by disease or by surgical excision takes place, not from the stump of the absent part, but by the continued growth of the remaining liver lobes.[13]

Anomalies of the veins of the liver. The intimate relation of the liver with the food-bearing veins seems fundamental, yet a few cases have been reported, one from this hospital [14] and one in a dog,[15] in which no vein from any source enters the liver (Fig. 43). The liver is small and compact, hanging from the centrum of the diaphragm with no falciform ligament ventrally and no connection with the caval fold dorsally—hence no lesser peritoneal cavity. The hepatic vein drains the organ, but the only entering vessel is the hepatic artery, much enlarged; yet on section the liver appears perfectly normal except for the absence of portal-vein branches and the too numerous arterial vessels in the portal canals. The sinusoids are normal in size and relation to the parenchyma in spite of their present technically capillary (arteriovenous) status. The inferior vena cava is transferred to the azygos system to enter the heart from above; the common mesenteric venous trunk runs behind the liver, is joined by the hepatic vein, and enters the heart from below. The food-bearing blood must have passed through the lungs before reaching the liver.

In considering the cause of this curious anomaly it is safe to assume that the presence of the hepatic vein and of the sinusoids indicates the earlier presence, at least for a while, of an entering vein, for the sinusoids are the result of the multiple interruptions of a continuous vessel. Perhaps the later loss of this entering vein may

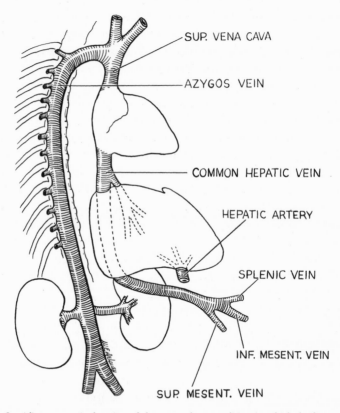

SUP. VENA CAVA

AZYGOS VEIN

COMMON HEPATIC VEIN

HEPATIC ARTERY

SPLENIC VEIN

INF. MESENT. VEIN

SUP. MESENT. VEIN

Fig. 43. Semidiagrammatic drawing of the anomalous condition in which the liver received no entering vein, but was supplied solely by an enlarged hepatic artery. The caudal part of the inferior vena cava is transferred to the azygos system to enter the heart from above; the common mesenteric trunk runs behind the liver, is joined by the hepatic vein, and enters the heart from below. [From G. Hellweg, Arch. Pa. 57, 426 (1954).]

be explained on the supposition that of the two original vitelline veins, one on each side of the intestine, the right member ran a more dorsal course than usual and thus made no contact with the liver bud growing ventrally from the gut. Above the dorsal anastomosis of the two vitelline veins, after the formation of the lower periduodenal venous ring, two pathways would then be offered for the intestinal blood, one interrupted by the hepatic sinusoids, the other running behind the liver without interruption, and of these the latter would surely prevail. The portal vein would gradually degenerate; the liver would remain small, and by its failure to reach either the ventral or the dorsal abdominal wall would exclude the umbilical circulation, prevent the normal formation of the vena cava inferior, and force the veins of the lower body to retain their original azygos connections (p. 89). The final atresia and disappearance of the portal vein must have occurred after the seventh week of embryonic life, for only during that week does the hepatic artery first enter the porta of the liver.

In another similar case, although no portal vein was present, the falciform ligament was normal and the markings on the under surface of the liver offered clear proof of the former presence of an umbilical vein. The only entering blood, after birth, came by way of the hepatic artery. This case is probably similar to that just described, except that in this infant the liver made a more extensive early growth to the ventral body wall, thus permitting the normal connections of the sinusoids with the left umbilical vein.

Pancreas. The pancreas develops from two entirely distinct entodermal outgrowths, known as the dorsal and ventral pancreas, respectively, which soon fuse to make a single organ. The dorsal pancreas grows out from the dorsal surface of the duodenal portion of the foregut a little above the level of the liver diverticulum in man, below it in many other mammals, and by the sixth week has already produced branching sprouts spreading in the dorsal mesentery. The ventral pancreas appears a little earlier as a bud on the caudal side of the root of the liver diverticulum [16] (Fig. 44, *A*), sometimes in the angle, sometimes definitely on the diverticulum or on the intestinal wall. Since this bud is to become the main pancreatic duct in man, the variation in its point of origin explains its variable adult relations with the bile duct at their entrance into the duodenum, where the two ducts may open together at the duodenal papilla, may open into an ampulla before entering, or may have entirely separate mouths at varying distances apart.

Whatever its exact relation with the hepatic diverticulum, the ventral pancreas, while still a mere bud, accompanies the bile duct in its dextral migration to the dorsal surface of the duodenum, and there sends its sprouts also into the dorsal mesentery. Since the dorsal pancreas, at a higher level on the duodenum, is not affected by this migration, the sprouts of the two pancreatic outgrowths meet and mingle in the same dorsal mesentery, and there the two ducts anastomose at a single point (Fig. 44, *B, C*). Thereafter the pancreas is a single organ with two ducts, either one of which may drain all the acini. In man the duct of the ventral pancreas (of Wirsung) is commonly the larger and the more constant, but that of the dorsal pancreas (of Santorini) remains patent in a large percentage of cases, and may become the only outlet by the obliteration of the ventral duct, as is the case normally in many animals.

The pancreatic ducts divide irregularly for many generations without change of epithelium before the terminal acini appear, and until birth the production of actively secreting tissue is slow, as befits a gland of the intestinal series; but the pancreas is by no means idle during the fetal period, for its second function, the production of the pancreatic islands, goes on actively during the latter portion

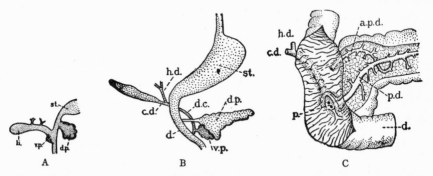

Fig. 44. Diagrams of the pancreas in embryos of (A) 6 weeks, (B) 7 weeks. (C) dissection of duodenum and pancreas in adult. *a.p.d.*, accessory pancreatic duct; *c.d.*, cystic duct; *d.*, duodenum; *d.c.*, ductus choledochus; *d.p.*, dorsal pancreas; *h.d.*, hepatic duct; *li.*, liver diverticulum; *p.*, duodenal papilla; *p.d.*, pancreatic duct; *st.*, stomach; *v.p.*, ventral pancreas. From J. L. Bremer and H. L. Weatherford, *Textbook of histology* (Blakiston Div., McGraw-Hill, New York, ed. 6, 1944).]

of pregnancy. The islands, or islets of Langerhans, develop along the course of, or at the ends of, a series of small anastomosing solid cords, branching from the smaller pancreatic ducts (Fig. 45). So minute and inconspicuous are these cords that they remained unsuspected until the early part of this century.[17] The islands themselves are composed of solid cords or masses of specialized cells in close relation with a net of blood capillaries, and are therefore ductless glands. They become active, producing their chief secretion, insulin, during the last few fetal months, and therefore before the acinar secretion begins to flow. This fact was utilized in securing from the pancreas of fetal calves a supply of insulin free from the digestive action of pancreatin. Later the hormone has been secured from certain fish, in which the islet tissue is entirely separate from the acinar tissue, or from the whole pancreas by neutralizing the acinar secretion, leaving only the islet secretion.

The ventral pancreatic bud may be bilobed, as is the lung bud higher up on the foregut. There are indications that this is its normal state, and that the left member normally degenerates very early. Occasionally the left bud may remain and develop its own pancreatic lobe, which, in the absence of a ventral mesentery, grows around the left side of the duodenum in the duodenal adventitia to join the other two parts of the pancreas in the dorsal mesentery. This condition, the persistence of both ventral ducts, is known as the ring form of the pancreas (Fig. 46, *A*) and may cause constriction of the second portion of the duodenum.

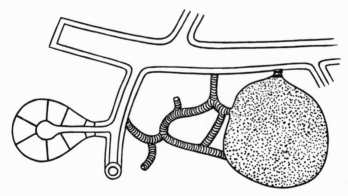

Fig. 45. Diagram showing the development of a pancreatic island from numerous solid branches of the ducts leading to the pancreatic acini.

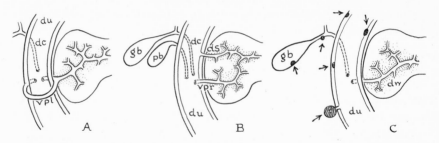

Fig. 46. Diagrams of (A) annular pancreas, (B) pancreatic bladder (in cat), (C) various positions and forms of accessory pancreas (arrows). *dc,* common bile duct; *dS, dW,* ducts of Santorini and Wirsung; *du,* duodenum; *gb,* gall bladder; *pb,* pancreatic bladder; *vpl, vpr,* left and right ventral pancreas.

Instead of growing around the duodenum, the left pancreatic lobe may follow the liver ducts for a variable distance toward the gall bladder. In this position it may be in the form of a pancreatic nodule,[18] or, very rarely in man, more frequently in other animals, it may remain tubular with a bulbous terminal enlargement,[19] the pancreatic bladder (Fig. 46, *B*), reminiscent of the hepatic duct and its gall bladder. Less than a dozen of these bladders have been recognized in men, but others may have been mistaken for cases of double gall bladder with divided cystic and common bile ducts, from which they may be distinguished only by minute histological differences.[20] The pancreatic bladders may, by the degeneration of their ducts, become isolated cysts, varying in size and situated at any point along the course of the cystic or common bile ducts. This possibility should be considered in all cases of cysts in the region of the curve of the duodenum.

Accessory pancreatic material is not uncommon and may be found anywhere along the foregut from the end of the oesophagus to the tip of Meckel's diverticulum. It mostly represents the ventral component and therefore is situated on the lesser curvature of the stomach or on the antimesenteric surface of the gut, but its occasional presence on other surfaces indicates that the dorsal pancreas may also be represented. The so-called accessory pancreas may be in the form of a small lobule, complete with duct and acini, of a misplaced pancreatic bladder,[21] or merely of a few pancreatic cells within the local mucosa. In this last position, since the active pancreatic cells are not protected by their secretion from the action of the acid in the gastric juice, as are the cells normally lining the stomach and upper bowel, it is probable that their presence may predispose to gastric or duodenal ulcer. Accessory pancreatic cells may also be found on the common bile duct and on the cystic duct, both derived from the original hepatic diverticulum, and even on the gall bladder, always on the primarily caudal surface, opposite to the liver and the hepatic duct. The accessory glands do not contain island cells.

Anatomical atresia of the main intrinsic pancreatic ducts is very rare. If it does occur, completely blocking the entrance of pancreatic secretion into the duodenum, the condition of meconium ileus results. In the presence of bile without the addition of pancreatic secretion the meconium or faeces become extremely sticky and viscid and readily obstruct the intestine below. A much more common cause for meconium ileus, however, is the condition known as pancreatic fibrosis, in which the secretion of the pancreatic acini is of a sticky mucous type, not flowing freely and therefore remaining as an inspissated mass in the terminal ducts and acini. With this the fibrous tissue of the gland may increase. This is actually a part of a generalized disease which may also manifest itself in the oral and tracheal glands as well as those of the intestine, called generalized mucoviscidosis.[22] Though causing meconeum ileus, it is obviously not an anatomical anomaly.

6 ——

URINARY SYSTEM AND

SUPRARENAL GLAND

The elimination of the waste products produced during the functional activity of the cells of the body is accomplished in various ways in different orders of animals. In the segmented worms the waste products are excreted into the coelom, from which they are eliminated by means of tiny tubules, one pair for each segment, leading almost directly to the surface of the body. The inner opening of each tubule is funnel-shaped and provided with cilia, which may have a regulatory function. Near this opening is a glomerulus, formed by a knot of capillaries in intimate relation with a specially modified portion of the mesothelial lining of the coelom, by means of which waste products of distant cells, transported in the blood, can be added to the coelomic fluid for elimination through the nearby tubule. The modification consists of the production, in the epithelial layer covering the glomerulus, of excessively thin plates or films of protoplasm investing the blood capillaries, the two layers forming an osmotic membrane for fluid and chemical exchange, similar to the protoplasmic films in the lung alveoli (p. 35) for the exchange of oxygen and carbondioxide.

In the chordates, this general plan persists, but with important changes. Segmental tubules still drain from the coelom by ciliated, funnel-shaped mouths, with a glomerulus in relation with each, but they all connect with two longitudinal ducts, running caudally on each side of the body to the cloaca, and thence to the surface. Both tubules and ducts develop from the narrow neck of the somite, called the *nephrotome,* by which the somite is connected with the outer and inner walls of the coelom (Fig. 47, *a*). Both the somite and its neck are originally hollow structures, containing minute mesial prolongations of the coelomic cavity. The proximal end of the nephrotome separates from the somite, turns laterally, and after a few coils runs caudally as a longitudinal duct, which in turn is joined by each succeeding nephrotome. The lateral end of the nephrotome preserves its funnel-shaped opening into the coelom; cilia grow within the funnel, and a glomerulus develops in relation with it, either in the neighboring coelomic wall or in the wall of the tubule itself within the ciliated mouth (*b*). Eight or more such tubules and the accompanying duct on each side form a pronephros, and its duct is the pronephric duct. This is the sole type of excretory organ in

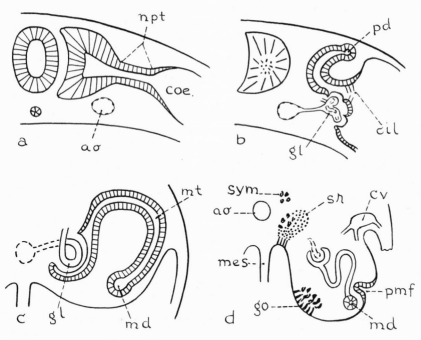

Fig. 47. Diagrams to show derivation of pronephros and mesonephros (*a, b, c*). Diagram (*d*) shows origin of the paramesonephric (Müllerian) duct, the gonad, and the suprarenal gland from mesonephric peritoneum. *ao*, aorta; *cil*, cilia; *coe*, coelom; *cv*, posterior cardinal vein; *gl*, glomerulus; *go*, gonad; *md*, mesonephric duct; *mes*, mesentery; *mt*, mesonephric tubule; *npt*, nephrotome; *pd*, pronephric duct; *pmf*, paramesonephric funnel; *sr*, suprarenal cortex; *sym*, sympathetic ganglion.

the chordates, and it is present as a vestigeal organ in all vertebrates, including man. It is located in the upper vertebral levels, cervical and upper thoracic, and in older human embryos small cysts occasionally occur at the root of the neck which are recognizable by their cuboidal epithelium as being of pronephric origin, but it is doubtful if any persist after birth.

As more and more segments are added caudally with the growth of the embryo, a new type of urinary organ develops from the succeeding nephrotomes. This second type is represented by the paired mesonephroi or Wolffian bodies. In this organ the nephrotome is cut off at both ends, so that ciliated mouths no longer are present and all continuity with the coelom is lost. A glomerulus, supplied by a branch of the adjacent aorta (Fig. 47, c), develops in relation with the lateral end of each nephrotome, and the mesial end curves laterally to join the pronephric duct of the same side, which now becomes known as the mesonephric or Wolffian duct. In this excretory organ, then, all direct drainage from the coelom is discarded and full reliance is placed on the activity of the tubular and glomerular epithelium. It should be noted, however, that (as in the pronephros) the nephrotomes, and hence the tubules derived from them, originally contain a portion of the general coelom, that their component cells are by derivation coelomic epithelium, and also that the tubules do not produce their own duct but open individually into ducts already provided by the pronephros. The excretory system and the duct system are separate entities.

The mesonephric tubules are longer and larger than those of the pronephros, and their more extensive coils form, on either side, a longitudinal ridge on the dorsal wall of the coelom. At first limited to the thoracic region, the tubules increase in number by the addition of new members from successively more caudal nephrotomes until at about 5 weeks, in man, they extend to the third lumbar segment. From then on the most cranial tubules degenerate rapidly, reducing the total number and giving the false impression of the caudal migration of the whole organ. By 8 weeks no tubules remain active, and the human mesonephroi cease to exist as renal organs. As will be explained later (p. 111), however, a few of the degenerating tubules and the mesonephric ducts remain, and serve as the outlets for the genital products in the male (epididymis and ductus deferens), while in the female they become constant vestigeal structures (epoöphoron, paroöphoron). In the male the lower ends of both mesonephric ducts turn mesially and open side by side into that part of the urogenital sinus which is to become the prostatic urethra. In the female they are obliterated or remain vestigeal.

Veins of the mesonephros. Along all its length the lateral border of each mesonephric ridge lies just ventral to the posterior cardinal vein (Fig. 47, *d*), which responds to this propinquity by sending numerous branches among the coiled tubules (Fig. 48, *A*), where they form a close-meshed net of thin-walled vessels. Gradually

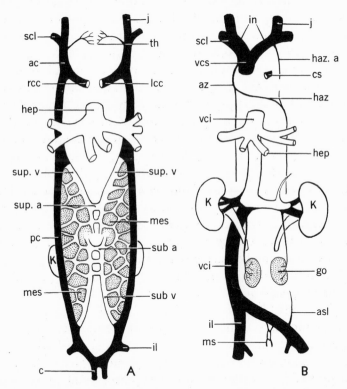

Fig. 48. The transformation of the posterior cardinal system of veins: (A) embryonic; (B) fetal. *ac,* anterior cardinal; *asl,* ascending lumbar; *az,* azygos; *c,* caudal; *cs,* coronary sinus; *go,* gonad; *haz,* hemiazygos; *haz.a,* accessory hemiazygos; *hep,* hepatic; *il,* common iliac; *in,* innomate; *j.* jugular; *k,* kidney; *lcc,* left common cardinal; *mes,* mesonephros; *ms,* median sacral; *pc,* posterior cardinal; *rcc,* right common cardinal; *scl,* subclavian; *sub a, sub v,* subcardinal anastomosis and vein; *sup a, sup v,* supracardinal anastomosis and vein; *th,* thyroid branches; *vci, vcs,* vena cava inferior, superior.

through the net a second longitudinal vessel, called the subcardinal vein, becomes distinct along the medial border of each ridge, near the root of the mesentery, and makes a few anastomoses with its fellow of the opposite side through the loose mesenchymal tissue of this root. Through this subcardinal anastomosis, the veins from the left kidney, from the left adrenal gland, and from the left members of the genital apparatus can join those from the right side, which then join the hepatic veins to play an important part in the formation of the vena cava inferior (p. 89). Cranial to this anastomosis each subcardinal vein is replaced by another longitudinal vessel, the supracardinal vein, running in a slightly more dorsal position. (To the embryologist, familiar with transverse sections of embryos as seen through the microscope, the prefixes "sub" or "supra" naturally apply to the positions ventral or dorsal to the plane of the aorta.) The two supracardinal veins anastomose dorsal to the aorta, and later become the azygos system, the anastomosis and the left supracardinal vein supplying the hemazygos portion; and, as the cranial ends of the mesonephroi and the posterior cardinal veins degenerate, the azygos system takes over the segmental veins of the body wall. At the same time, the two anterior cardinal veins form an anastomosis through the peri-intestinal capillary plexus serving the thymus and the thyroid gland (later to become the left innominate vein), and normally after this link is established, perhaps because of the right-sided dominance of the inferior vena cava, all connection between the azygos system and the left anterior cardinal vein is lost; both the hemiazygos and the azygos veins open into the right common cardinal vein, which is to become the proximal portion of the superior vena cava.

Occasionally, however, portions of the original pattern may remain as anomalies. The cranial portion of the left azygos system may persist as the accessory hemiazygos vein (Fig. 48, *B*), a branch of the left innominate vein; more rarely, the original bilateral condition prevails, resulting in double superior vena cava, or in the presence of the oblique vein of Marshall. Obliteration of the normal right-sided drainage produces the rare left superior vena cava. Also, almost any path may be chosen through the two capillary plexuses concerned—the peri-intestinal and that in the mesonephros—and through their connected venous trunks; and, as an added complication, since certain anomalies of the pulmonary veins are also related to the presence of the peri-intestinal plexus (p. 43), these veins also may be included in variations of the azygos and cardinal-vein complex. Recently the many anomalous patterns already known have been given by Winter.[1] Other less distinct longitudinal pathways through the mesonephric venous net have also been described, but these are apparently inconstant in man. The viscera that develop in or migrate into the region formerly occupied by the mesonephros—kidney, testis or ovary, adrenal gland—appropriate certain of its venous channels for their own drainage, and these vessels may conceivably share in one of the recorded anomalies.

The kidney or metanephros is the third and final urinary organ, and like the mesonephros it is formed by the union of an excretory system and a duct system. The latter develops as a bud from the dorsolateral side of each mesonephric duct near its entrance into the urogenital sinus. The bud grows out in tubular form (the ureter) and enlarges terminally as a blind pouch (the renal pelvis) (Fig. 49, *A*); each pelvis soon meets and is partially enclosed by a compact mass of mesodermal tissue, called the metanephrogenic tissue or renal blastema, supposed to be formed by the undifferentiated nephrotomes of the more caudal somites. This dense tissue applies

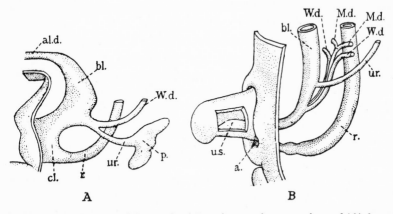

Fig. 49. The development of the renal pelvis and ureter; human embryo of (A) 6 weeks, (B) 9 weeks. (Keibel.) *a,* anus; *al.d.,* allantoic duct; *bl.* bladder; *cl.,* cloaca; *M.d.,* para-mesonephric duct; *p.,* renal pelvis; *r.,* rectum; *ur.,* ureter; *u.s.,* urogenital sinus; *W.d.,* mesonephric duct. [From J. L. Bremer and H. L. Weatherford, *Textbook of histology* (Blakiston Div., McGraw-Hill, New York, ed. 6, 1944).]

itself to the distal surfaces of the renal pelvis, and is to supply the excretory system of the combined gland, for which the ureteric bud and its branches make the duct system.

Although the ureter is primarily a branch of the mesonephric duct, it soon attains a more independent status. With further growth the urogenital sinus expands and takes into its own wall the terminal portion of the two mesonephric ducts, so that the ducts and the ureters now open by separate mouths. The mesonephric ducts open close together near the median line, with the two ureters in a lateral position, and by the unequal growth of adjacent parts of the sinus wall the ureters are then carried to a higher level and enter cranial to the ducts (Fig. 49, *B*). The sinus is later differentiated into bladder above and urethra below, the neck of the bladder and internal sphincter coming between the two sets of openings.

The pelvis of the kidney develops two pouches, the major calices, upper and lower, and from each of these bud off smaller pouches, the minor calices (Fig. 50), of which there may be 15 to 20, each representing the pelvis of a simple kidney such as is found in the cat or rabbit; the human kidney is multiple. Finally, from the flattened top of each minor calyx (produced in a complicated fashion) grow out 20–30 papillary ducts, which in turn produce many generations of branches; these are the collecting tubules. This branching continues until birth or later. All of the structures already mentioned are derived from the ureteric bud of the mesonephric duct, and form the duct system of the kidney.

The active glandular portion of the kidney is provided by the renal blastema or nephrogenic tissue, already mentioned. The pelvis grows into this mass and every minor calyx is surrounded by it. In it certain cells group themselves in the form of small vesicles (Fig. 51), one of which applies itself to one of the branches at each division of the collecting tubules, and then repeats the story of the mesonephric nephrotomes, in that each vesicle becomes oval, lengthens and coils to become a convoluted tubule, forms a glomerulus at one end, and opens at the other into the duct, as represented by the collecting tubule.[2] The addition of Henle's loop (not recognizable in either pronephric or mesonephric tubules) in the course of the renal tubule may indicate a refinement in the process of urinary excretion not necessary in the younger embryo.[3] Gen-

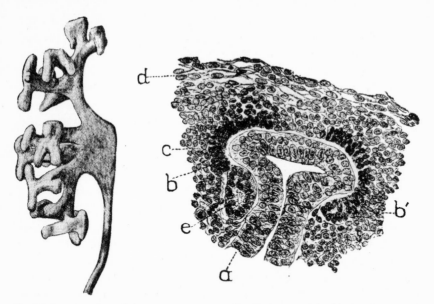

Fig. 50. Reconstruction of the ureter, renal pelvis and its branches in a human embryo of 7 weeks. (Huber.) [From J. L. Bremer and H. L. Weatherford, *Textbook of histology* (Blakiston Div., McGraw-Hill, New York, ed. 6, 1944).]

Fig. 51. Section of the distal end of a renal collecting tubule in a human embryo of eight weeks. (Huber.) *a*, primary collecting tubule; *b,b*, inner layer, and *c*, outer layer of dense mesenchyma (renal blastema); *d*, loose mesenchyma; *e*, vesicle, origin of renal tubule. [From J. L. Bremer and H. L. Weatherford, *Textbook of histology* (Blakiston Div., McGraw-Hill, New York, ed. 6, 1944).]

eration after generation of tubules and glomeruli are added peripherally as long as the collecting tubules continue to branch. In the fetal kidney of the latter part of pregnancy, one may see various stages of the development of glomeruli, from the youngest, near the surface of the cortex, to the functional stage, nearer the pelvic border.

From their original position in the pelvis of the body the kidneys normally migrate cranially while still in the formative state. Rarely one kidney remains abnormally in the pelvic position. On leaving the pelvis both kidneys must crowd through the crotch formed by the two umbilical arteries, the end branches of the abdominal aorta (Fig. 52). This brings them close together, and occasionally the two blastemas fuse, almost invariably at the lower poles, causing the

Fig. 52. Diagrams showing the migration of kidneys from pelvis: (A) in pelvis; (B) between umbilical arteries, where lower poles may fuse; (C) kidneys free to migrate upward; (D) horseshoe form caught under inferior mesenteric artery.

condition known as "horseshoe kidney." The two ureters pass in front of the conjoined portion. In this form the kidneys almost always remain at the lower lumbar level, further migration being prevented by the root of the inferior mesenteric artery. However, it is possible, if one half of the conjoined organ is dominant, for the dominant half to draw the lesser half to its side and continue its migration upward. Such a case resembles a double kidney arising from two ureteric buds on one side, with agenesis of the kidney on the other; it can be distinguished from this condition by the courses and connections of the two ureters.

After leaving the pelvic cavity the growing kidney continues to travel cranially, following a retroperitoneal course along the dorsal abdominal wall. During most of its course the kidney lies dorso-mesial to the mesonephros, and receives its veins from the mesonephric venous net, and through this drains into the subcardinal veins and their anastomosis (inferior vena cava). The distance traveled by the kidney in this ascent is actually only three or four somites; the apparently greater length of the ureters is chiefly due to the straightening of the embryonic spinal curves and the growth of the vertebral bodies. At about the eighth week, 20 mm, each kidney is met head on by the caudally migrating suprarenal or adrenal gland of the same side, which in human embryos is an especially large organ. Further migration ceases for both organs, but for the suprarenal gland this meeting is not the cause of the cessation, for at this level the gland becomes involved in the formation of the diaphragm and thereby its position is fixed, even if the kidney is not present at its normal level. The kidney, on the other hand, may migrate farther, for, in the very rare cases of agenesis of one suprarenal gland and the consequent dorsal hiatus of the diaphragm, the corresponding kidney may pass through the hiatus and invade the thorax.

Anomalies of the ureters. Occasionally the ureteric bud of one side fails to develop, or, on the other hand, supernumerary buds may arise from the mesonephric ducts. The great number of these found in early embryos as compared with their rarity in the adult shows that many are resorbed in utero, but some may remain as shorter or longer blind pockets or may produce supernumerary kidneys. The anomalous renal pelvis may fuse with the normal pelvis of that side, or more commonly the two blastemas may fuse, giving the appearance of a double ureter from one kidney with either a single or a double pelvis.[4] After the absorption of the mouth of the mesonephric duct into the dorsolateral wall of the urogenital sinus and the change in position of ureters and mesonephric ducts, these extra ureters commonly open by separate mouths and usually into the bladder; but ureteric buds arising from the mesonephric duct far cranial to the main ureter of that side may be carried with the duct to the lower part of the urogenital sinus distal to the cystic sphincter, and there open into the urethra, with resulting incontinence. It is important to remember that the lower ureteral opening is always that from the upper kidney or upper pole of a conjoined kidney, and that the two ureters are thus always crossed, with danger of possible obstruction to one or both. If such a displaced accessory ureteric bud does not meet the blastema, it will remain as a blindly ending tube, perhaps with a terminal expansion representing the renal pelvis.

The ureters are also subject to intrinsic malformations, often similar to those in the intestinal tract. Diverticula are rarely found, but congenital stenoses occur occasionally, often in the form of a thin transverse perforated veil and mostly in the lower part of the tube; if such a stenosis is in the intramural portion of the tube, as the ureter passes through the bladder wall, it may cause a bulging of the bladder muscles into the bladder cavity, an intravesicular cyst or ureterocele.[5] Valvelike folds of the mucosa are also found occasionally, most often at the two ends of the ureter. Closure of the ureter from any one of these causes may lead to expansion of the renal pelvis, which if sufficiently severe may lead to destruction of the cortical structure (hydronephrosis), and to a great enlargement of the ureter (hydroureter). Congenital megaloureter, like megacolon, is probably due to derangement of the neuromuscular system in a juxtacystic segment, which leads both to loss of peristaltic action and more especially to loss of tone in the ureter above, without which the wall is unable to withstand pressure from within.[6]

Anomalies of the renal vessels. During their migration, the kidneys are constantly supplied by the neighboring blood vessels, making new regional connections and dropping the old as they progress. Rarely, certain of the old connections remain as anomalous vessels, usually accessory. Thus anomalous renal arteries may arise as branches of the middle sacral artery, of the iliac artery (a branch of the umbilical), of lumbar arteries, or of the inferior mesenteric root. These enter the lower pole of the organ, and may cross ventral to the ureter and thus cause an intermittent or permanent blockage of the urine. In its final location, also, the early kidney may receive accessory branches from the phrenic or suprarenal arteries, entering the upper pole. In the rare cases of thoracic kidney the total blood supply is local, from the appropriate intercostal arteries. Anomalous renal veins have a similar range. During most of the migration, however, the main renal supply is from the numerous mesonephric arteries by dorsal branches which join the embryonic capillary plexus lying in the renal hylus. In many mammals one of these mesonephric branches becomes the permanent renal artery, but in man by the time the kidney has reached its normal location the mesonephric tubules of the region and their corresponding arteries are degenerating, and, at about 8 weeks, an appropriately placed member of the periaortic capillary plexus on each side suddenly enlarges and assumes arterial character to become the definite renal artery.[7]

Congenital cysts of the kidney. The addition of new glomeruli at the surface of the cortex is accompanied after a while by the degeneration of the older, centrally placed ones. Three or more generations of the latter are affected,[8] and occasionally some of these may remain as cysts near the individual minor calices. Also the branching of the collecting tubules may cease while some of the surface nephrogenic tissue still remains; in the absence of available collecting tubules with which to join, attempted glomerulus and tubule formation may continue, resulting in multiple cysts over the surface of the kidney and in the center of the renal columns. Finally, similar cysts from nonunion of the collecting tubule and nephrogenic vesicle may be produced throughout the cortex, occasionally leaving insufficient active renal tissue to ensure continued life. The epithelium lining these cysts may be cuboidal or flattened by internal pressure, and attempts at tubule formation may make some of the cysts multilocular. This cystic condition is said to be hereditary.

Does the fetal kidney excrete? In the bird before hatching the mesonephros is a large organ and continues active until the kidney is sufficiently developed to take over the excretory function. The urine from both sources is poured from the cloaca into the allantois, which is expanded distally as a large sac. From the allantoic sac the fluid portion of the urine is resorbed by the activity of its epithelial walls and returned to the circulation, leaving the solids in crystal form within the sac; for the bird, being enclosed in a shell, must conserve its body fluids. This is true of all oviparous forms. In the pig and sheep, and in several other mammals with epithelio-chorial placentation, the mesonephros and kidney also overlap in function[9] and the urine is stored till birth in a large allantoic sac situated at the placental end of the umbilical cord, from which the fluid portion is returned to the circulation by the allantoic vessels. In man there is a period in which only a few mesonephric nephrons persist and either few or no renal nephrons have reached a functional stage—a period in which fetal excretion is minimal or absent. During this interval fetal excretion is transferred to the haemo-chorial maternal placenta, and specifically to the placental villi, the epithelium of which displays the thin epithelial plates in close relation with underlying capillary blood vessels so characteristic of the osmotic membranes of the renal glomeruli.* Through this modified placenta the fetal excretory products are transferred to the maternal blood to be reëxcreted by the maternal kidneys.[10] In the latter part of pregnancy the fetal kidneys are

---

* Modern studies by the use of the electron microscope reveal significant differences in the structure of the thin epithelial plates of the renal glomeruli and those of the placental villi, and seem to indicate doubt as to their similarity of function. See G. B. Wislocki and E. W. Dempsey, "Electron microscopy of the human placenta," *Anat. Record 123*, 133–167 (1955).

undoubtedly potentially functional and urinary constituents are present in the amniotic fluid,[11] but the total quantity of these constituents is normally so small as to suggest that the placenta still bears the greater share of the burden. This extra work on the part of the maternal urinary organs may play a part in the occasional eclampsias of pregnancy. On the other hand, if the fetal urethra is blocked in any way, the bladder at birth is distended to enormous proportions. The reason for the normally partial inactivity of the apparently functional late-fetal kidneys until just before birth is not definitely known, but may be connected with known differences in maternal and fetal blood pressures, or with some antidiuretic hormone supplied by the fetal hypophysis.[12] Agenesis of one or both kidneys is not unknown, and in the latter case the death of the fetus seems due, not to anuria, but to the immaturity of the lungs.[13]

The urinary bladder has its own peculiar anomalies. It has already been said (p. 92) that the genitourinary sinus becomes expanded above as the bladder and constricted below as the urethra. Above the bladder the sinus is continuous with the proximal end of the allantois, following the ventral body wall to the umbilical cord.[14] Actually the bladder includes the expanded base of the allantois as well as the upper end of the sinus (Fig. 24, *E*), for even the uppermost of the rectovesical fistulae, presumably representing the upper limit of the cloaca (and urogenital sinus), open into the midportion of the bladder. This double origin of the bladder, from both sinus and allantois, may be marked by a constriction between the two parts, giving rise to the "hourglass" bladder (Fig. 53), or the constriction may lead to a perforated flat septum or even to complete separation of the two parts of the cavity, the allantoic portion then forming a urachal cyst.[15] Finally, the allantoic duct, which normally closes as the urachus, may persist in its primary condition, remaining open from the apex of the bladder through the umbilicus as a patent urachus.

Diverticula of the bladder and transverse or frontal septa dividing the bladder into two more or less equal, but always connected, portions have been noticed in the fetus, but only in a few instances, and the frequency of the diverticula in the adult makes it almost certain that this type usually develops late and is brought on by pulsion through a weakened muscularis. The septa are rare and may be caused by an especially strong muscle band in the wall of the fetal bladder, which remains small, drawing the septum across the cavity as the bladder enlarges. The very rare vertical or median sagittal septa may possibly be caused by the meeting and partial fusion of the dorsal and ventral walls of the "seat" of the saddle-shaped urogenital sinus. Such a fusion has not been recorded in the embryo, but the lumen along this line is then very narrow. The most striking anomaly of the bladder, exstrophy, is described in a later chapter (p. 122).

The lower portion of the urogenital sinus becomes the membranous urethra, opening through the urogenital plate. In the female this forms practically the whole urethra, but in the male this part is considerably lengthened by the addition of the penile portion derived from the genital tubercle (p. 119). In both sexes the urethra is subject to obstruction due to developmental stenosis or even atresia, sometimes veillike, though complete atresia is very rare. Rare also are small urethral diverticula. In the male, obstruc-

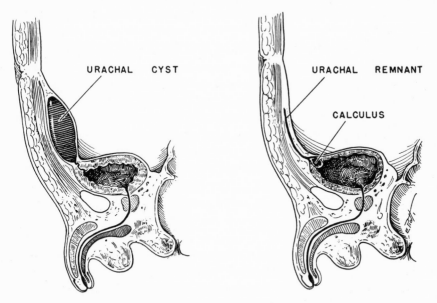

Fig. 53. (*left*) Sagittal view of urachal cyst connected with the bladder by a pinhole opening. (*right*) Sketch from a 7-year-old boy with a calculus in the lower end of a urachal tract. [From W. E. Ladd and R. E. Gross, *Abdominal surgery in infancy and childhood* (Saunders, Philadelphia, 1941).]

tive lesions may be caused by the presence of valves in the region of the verumontanum. This latter is the internal mound on the dorsal wall of the prostatic urethra through which the two mesonephric ducts enter; the abrupt mound lifts the overlying urethral mucosa, causing diagonal folds running both proximally and distally, and often, especially on the proximal side, the folds may be prominent and extend for some distance diagonally upward, making fairly efficient valves, presenting a marked obstruction to the outflow of urine, though by their nature they cannot be detected by ordinary instrumentation.

The suprarenal or adrenal glands. Although these organs have no functional connection with the urinary system, their only relation with the kidney being that of position, their embryological origin makes them proper subjects for discussion in this place. They belong to the ductless series and each comprises two different parts, separate organs in fishes, but in mammals brought together as the cortex and medulla of a combined gland. The cortex is derived from the mesothelial lining of the coelom continuous with that which covers the protruding mesonephros; the medulla is formed of cells migrating from the sympathetic ganglia of the region. The mesonephros by its very bulk produces a wide longitudinal ridge, projecting from the dorsal wall into the coelom and bounded by deep furrows, one between the ridge and the lateral body wall and the second between the ridge and the mesentery (Fig. 47, *d*). In the depth of the median furrow in the upper thoracic region the coelomic mesothelium becomes active during the fourth week of embryonic life and sends a group of solid cell cords into the underlying mesenchyma. These cords lose connection with the parent layer and move as a compact mass to meet the chain of sympathetic ganglia of the periaortic plexus. Certain cells of the ganglia change their character, become *chromaffin cells,* and infiltrate the mass of mesodermal cords to form the medulla of the organ, the mesothelial mass thus becoming its cortex. This cortical mass, however, does not persist in the adult gland. Only a few days after the original cell cords become separated from their parent mesothelium, a second proliferation occurs, this time from the same mesothelial layer, but from a more median region, immediately on either side of the root of the mesentery.[16] The new cells are small, with small dark-staining nuclei and basophilic protoplasm, in sharp contrast with the acidophilic cells with large clear nuclei of the earlier group, so that each type can be readily followed from their first appearance. The small dark cells form a layer three or four cells thick, which spreads over the surface of the original mass of large clear cells, gradually enclosing it and forming an outer, additional cortical layer.[17] The whole complex gland then acquires a capsule from the surrounding mesenchyma. From their future history, the original cell mass has been variously called the primitive, provisional, or fetal cortex, or X-zone, the later surface layer being named the definitive, permanent, or true cortex.

For some time the fetal cortex grows rapidly, and by the fourth month forms the greater part of the gland. Much of this bulk is due to numerous sinusoidal vessels which invade the cell mass from the medulla and transform it into an irregular network of cell cords. The component cells have vacuoles containing certain lipoids, and show all the signs of active secretion. The permanent cortex, meanwhile, grows more slowly, and at birth may still consist of a few layers of undifferentiated cells or may occupy a quarter or even a third of the cortical thickness. The fetal cortex then degenerates more rapidly than the other enlarges, with the result that at the end of the first year the gland weighs less than at birth and contains only the permanent type of cortex.

The meaning of this replacement of one type of suprarenal cortex by another so different is not known. The two types of cells can hardly elaborate the same or even similar secretions, although it is known that both do produce androgens.[18] One might speculate on the probable action of a product secreted by the provisional cortex that is apparently so necessary in the first half of intrauterine life and so progressively superfluous thereafter. Equally puzzling is the apparently constant association of anencephaly with the absence or early atrophy of the permanent cortex.[19]

In the human embryo the suprarenal glands develop precociously, so that at the time when the upper tubules of the mesonephroi begin to degenerate (5 weeks) the glands are large enough to jut out from the dorsal wall in their place, and as the mesonephroi make their apparent caudal migration the suprarenal glands migrate caudally in their wake, just in time to play a part in the closure of the pleuro-peritoneal passages. With further descent they meet the cranially migrating kidneys, and mold their form to the latter's superior poles. The level of this meeting marks the caudal limit of the suprarenal migration in any case, for if the kidney has not reached its proper level, whether from agenesis or in the condition of horseshoe kidney, the suprarenal gland retains its normal position in relation with the diaphragm, though it does not show its normal compressed shape.

Not infrequently accessory suprarenal glands are found arising from lower levels of the paravertebral furrow, some complete with both medulla and cortex, others with cortex alone, and these may appear in unexpected places. Thus, because of its origin from the mesonephric mesothelium near the similar origin of the gonads (Fig. 47, *d*), one of these masses may become enclosed within the capsule of its neighboring testis or ovary and be carried with it into the scrotum or broad ligament, as the case may be, as a small piece of adrenal cortex or as a complete, though small, gland. Only when both elements are present is the term accessory suprarenal gland properly applied to these scattered paravertebral masses. Conversely, small groups of chromaffin cells, up to 1 cm in size and resembling the suprarenal medulla in character, are found normally along the aorta, resting on the dorsal surface of the sympathetic ganglia from which they are derived.[20] They are called the paraganglia or aortic bodies, and are grouped as the chromaffin system, which includes also the suprarenal medulla.

7 ──────

UTERUS AND VAGINA,
GENITAL APPARATUS, AND
EXTERNAL GENITALIA

The peritoneal mesothelium covering each of the two mesonephric ridges produces two important structures. On the ventromedial borders it forms intrinsic portions of the gonads, which will be described later, while on the ventrolateral borders it gives rise to the Müllerian or paramesonephric ducts (Fig. 47, *d*), from which are to develop essential portions of the female genital system. At the seventh week of embryonic life this ventrolateral mesothelium near the cephalic end of each organ grows into the underlying mesenchyma in the form of a short longitudinal funnel-shaped groove. Each upper end remains open and flaring, while from the deeper cells of the lower end a slender solid cord grows caudally in the mesenchyma parallel with the mesonephric duct and on its lateral side. The solid cord soon becomes tubular, only the tip remaining solid. The two tubes continue caudally in this same position until they near the bottom of the mesonephroi, when they turn mesially, cross in front of the mesonephric ducts, and between them, meet each other and, side by side, continue again caudally to reach the urogenital sinus. During the eighth week the parallel portions fuse, and the conjoined tubes thus form a Y-shaped structure (Fig. 54).

The paramesonephric ducts develop in all embryos, whether they are to be male or female, for the embryo until about the ninth week is in an indifferent stage, before sexuality is declared, although genetically it is marked from conception by the presence or absence of the X-chromosome in its cell nuclei. In the male, after having fused and joined the sinus, at about the tenth week, both paramesonephric ducts normally disappear, except for the lower and upper ends, which persist as the prostatic utricle and the normally inconspicuous appendix testis, or hydatid, respectively. The latter, however, may become cystic and painfully swollen after birth (Fig. 60, *G*). The mesonephric ducts remain as the outlet for the male genital products, namely, the ductus epididymidis and the ductus deferens (Fig. 59). In the female, the fused portions of the paramesonephric ducts, the upright of the Y, form the uterus, while the arms of the Y become the uterine or Fallopian tubes, the initial funnel-shaped grooves remaining open as their fimbriated mouths; the mesonephric ducts degenerate, leaving only the inconstant Gartner's canals in the uterine wall and the ducts of the paroöphoron, the epoöphoron, and the appendix vesiculosa in the mesovarium (Fig. 55).

Anomalies of the uterus are to be expected from its method of formation. Failure of the two ducts to fuse leads to division of the uterus, either completely by a median septum or partially as a bifid uterus, and the rare absence of one uterine tube causes its own distinctive malformation. On the other hand, there may be two fimbriated openings on one side, showing duplication of the original funnel-shaped ingrowth; the extra tube may remain short, may join the primary tube at various levels or may complete its growth to the sinus, and thus produce another type of double uterus. Rarely the isolated lower end of a shorter accessory tube may be found in the broad ligament of the uterus, or as a cyst or nodule in the uterine muscle,[1] or may even become enclosed within the neighboring ovary, appearing later as a nodule of uterine tissue, recognizable by its special type of mucosa. Similar nodules are occasionally found also in the testis as a curious reminder of the indifferent stage of development. Duplications and diverticula of the main Fallopian (uterine) tubes may appear, similar to those in the intestine (p. 59), and ectopic pregnancies have been reported as occurring in these redundant tubes.

It used to be considered that both uterus and vagina are derived from the fused portion of the paramesonephric ducts, and that the

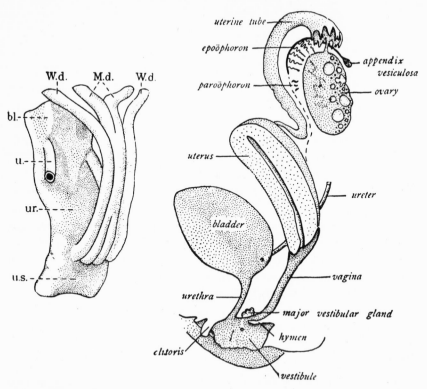

Fig. 54. Reconstruction showing the fusion of the paramesonephric (Müllerian) ducts to form the uterus. (Keibel.) *bl.,* bladder; *M.d.,* paramesonephric ducts; *u.,* ureter; *ur.,* urethra; *u.s.,* urogenital sinus; *W.d.,* mesonephric (Wolffian) duct. [From J. L. Bremer and H. L. Weatherford, *Textbook of histology* (Blakiston Div., McGraw-Hill, New York, ed. 6, 1944).]

Fig. 55. Diagram of the female genital organs. [From J. L. Bremer and H. L. Weatherford, *Textbook of histology* (Blakiston Div., McGraw-Hill, ed. 6, 1944).]

occasional median septa in both these organs, or even double uterus and vagina, were thus readily explained by failure of the normal fusion. More careful observations have shown, however, that after the blind ends of the ducts have made contact with the sinus wall, they withdraw again somewhat, but retain connection with the sinus by means of a solid cord of cells, originally double (Fig. 56). Opinions differ as to the origin of this solid cell cord or vaginal bulb; its cells may come from the paramesonephric ducts themselves,[2] or from the mesonephric ducts on either side,[3] or from the

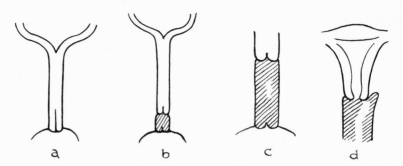

Fig. 56. Diagrams explaining the position of the epithelial cell cords (diagonal lines) joining the urogenital sinus with the ends of the paramesonephric ducts to form the vagina.

urogenital sinus by paired outgrowths from its dorsal wall.[4] The cell cord is variously described as forming only the lower part, or the whole,[5] of the vagina. In the former case, the differentiation into uterus above and vagina below takes place along the course of the fused portion of the paramesonephric ducts; in the latter case the uterus only is from the ducts, the vagina from the solid cell cord drawn from the sinus. The second idea suits better the abrupt change in structure at the uterovaginal border, but is the one least favored by present investigators.

These differences of opinion concerning the derivation of such an apparently simple structure as the vagina probably indicate the occurrence of variations either in the timing or in the actual extent of the embryological sequence involved in different types of embryo. Comparison with other mammals is sometimes a help in arriving at the truth, though it is also often misleading. For what it is worth it may be noted that in certain rodents the vagina is definitely derived from the sinus by splitting off from its dorsal wall. Certain anomalies of a region also often, but by no means infallibly, afford a clue to the development. One of the anomalies, recto-vaginal fistula, can best be explained as derived from an originally sinurectal fistula representing a portion of the cloaca (p. 59), for otherwise it would be exceedingly difficult to explain such a fistula between the rectum and the paramesonephric ducts, which only reach the urogenital sinus after the division of the cloaca is completed. If the fistula met the sinus in the region of the vaginal bulbs, it might readily be carried by their growth onto the vagina, and be transformed into a rectovaginal fistula. The opening of the fistula, which may be double, is most often in the lower third of the vagina, but may be as high as the posterior fornix. Another, rarer anomaly is the opening of a displaced ureter, usually from an accessory kidney, into the vagina, a condition that can best be understood by considering the vagina as a part of, or derived from, the urogenital sinus, into which the ureters normally open. From another point of view, the aberrant ends of accessory paramesonephric ducts occasionally found in the broad ligament or in the gonad are always of uterine tissue only, and show no signs of vaginal mucosa, as should be the case if they were normally to produce even a part of that organ. Even the occasional presence of a median septum causing bifid or double vagina need not indicate derivation from the two parallel paramesonephric ducts, for the solid epithelial plug is also described as double in origin. Thus both comparative embryology and the study of anomalies indicate the sinus origin of the whole vagina.

Whatever its origin, the vagina remains solid until late in fetal life, the lumen clogged by proliferated epithelial cells. The anterior and posterior fornices start as solid shovel-shaped outgrowths. A permanent lumen begins near the fornices and spreads in both directions (Fig. 56, *c, d*), reaching the lower end last. Here canalization is normally irregular, resulting in the formation of the hymen, and may be incomplete, leading to the type of atresia known as imperforate hymen. This condition often remains unnoticed until puberty, at which time the trapped menstrual flow produces a cyst-like swelling of the vagina known as haematocolpos. Occasionally a similar cystic vagina may be present at birth, caused by the premature activity of the cervical glands of the uterus (hydrocolpos), due to the excess of maternal estrogens occasionally transmitted to the fetus at that time, which also is responsible for the not infrequent neonatal activity of the mammary glands (witch's milk) in both sexes. Within a few days, normally, both mammary glands and uterus revert to inactivity until puberty. With excessive menstrual flow or excessive activity of the cervical glands in the presence of an imperforate hymen, the swelling may include the uterus also, vagina and uterus forming one huge cyst, a condition known as haematometracolpos at puberty or hydrometracolpos at birth. The enormous size to which one of these cysts may grow can cause pressure on the neighboring urethra and rectum, with obstruction. The uterine walls may be stretched so thin that at birth hydrometracolpos has been mistaken for anterior meningocele or some other cyst or tumor, and removed by operation, with resulting sacrifice of uterus, tubes, and vagina.

Gonads. The peritoneal mesothelium of the dorsal wall of the coelom, including that covering the two mesonephric ridges, seems to be peculiarly active. The cords of the adrenal cortex are derived by ingrowth of this mesothelium in the groove between the mesonephric ridge and the mesentery (p. 100), and by similar ingrowth on the ventrolateral surface of each ridge the mesothelium forms the funnel-shaped depression and caudally running tube that are the precursors of the uterus and uterine tubes. Between these two centers of growth on the ventromedial border of each mesonephric ridge (Fig. 47, *d*), the mesothelium over a considerable longitudinal area becomes altered to form the genital or sex glands, or gonads. The surface cells increase in height and in number, and the underlying mesenchymal cells also multiply rapidly. Together these altered cells form the prominent genital ridge bulging from the already present mesonephric ridge (Fig. 57). During the seventh week, certain conspicuous, large, clear cells, the primary sex cells, appear among the cylindrical cells of the mesothelial layer and soon invade the underlying tissue, each sex cell or group of sex cells surrounded by a protective coating of mesothelial cells massed in the form of an irregular cord still connected with the surface layer.

The importance of these sex cells, not only because they apparently retain the totipotential characteristics of the fertilized ovum, but also because, from the point of view of the pathologist, they may form the basis for the future unregulated growth of all the germ layers found in the mixed tumors and teratomas, has caused many investigators to seek their ultimate origin and the method of their transportation to the gonads. Apparently they do not arise in situ, for no immature forms are found there to indicate their differentiation from mesothelial cells. It would be satisfactory to find that such apparently primitive cells arise directly or indirectly from the primitive knot (Hensen's node) of the early embryo, from which the three germ layers of the embryonic body take their origin, but of this there is no sound proof. Both their origin and their mode of transportation remained until recently in doubt. In embryos submitted to the common methods of fixation and staining the primitive sex cells are usually indistinguishable, in the early days, from the other cells by which they are surrounded. By modern histochemical techniques,[6] however, it is now possible to recognize these sex cells at their first appearance. They arise [7, 8] in the ento-dermal layer of the dorsal wall of the yolk sac, the future hindgut, caudal to the node, either from the entodermal cells or, more prob-ably, from primitive stem cells which are also the source of the entoderm, and from there migrate to the underlying mesenchyma of the gut wall and to its mesothelial coat, and in both these layers continue through the mesentery to the dorsal body wall and the genital folds. During this migration they produce pseudopodia and show frequent mitoses. In the loose tissue at the base of the mesen-

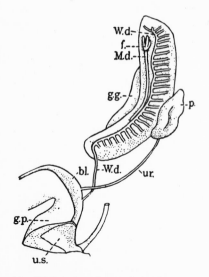

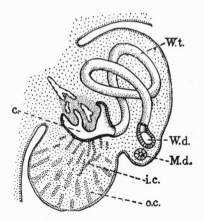

Fig. 57. Relation of genital gland to meso-nephros. From a reconstruction of an embryo of 6 weeks. *bl.*, bladder; *f*, fimbria, *g.g.*, genital gland; *g.p.*, genital papilla; *M.d.*, paramesonephric (Müllerian) duct; *p*. renal pelvis; *ur*, ureter; *u.s.*, urogenital sinus; *W.d.*, mesonephric duct. [From J. L. Bremer and H. L. Weatherford, *Textbook of histology* (Blakiston Div., McGraw-Hill, New York, ed. 6, 1944).]

Fig. 58. Diagram of the union of the testis cords with a mesonephric glomerular cap-sule. *c.*, glomerular capsule; *i.c.*, inner or rete cords; *M.d.*, paramesonephric duct; *o.c.*, outer or sex cords; *W.d.*, *W.t.*, meso-nephric duct, tubule. [From J. L. Bremer and H. L. Weatherford, *Textbook of histol-ogy* (Blakiston Div., McGraw-Hill, New York, ed. 6, 1944).]

tery certain of these primordial sex cells may go astray and wander to some distant region of the body, where, after lying dormant for a variable period because of the unfavorable surroundings, they may later become reactivated as the nucleus of some type of mixed neoplasm. Recently, however, other authors [9] claim that the identification of these cells is unreliable, that the methods used apply to any metabolically active cells nearing mitosis, and that the true germ cells are first developed within the simple cuboidal epithelium covering the gland itself, and can be traced from there into the germinal cords.

The change from the indifferent gonad to the definitive sex organ is seen first in the testis. At 8 weeks the cell cords of the testis containing the spermatogonia lose connection with the surface mesothelium by the ingrowth of the connective tissue tunica albuginea and become converted into clear-cut rounded cords, branching and anastomosing, in a bed of loose mesenchyma. Soon a definite pattern of the cords is discernible,[10] consisting of radial trunks joined to each other by three sets of arching branches, outer, middle, and inner. Future lengthening causes the arches to become greatly convoluted, but the pattern still persists, the coils of each arch remaining in a group and forming a vascular unit in that each group is supplied by a terminal artery. The radial portions remain relatively uncoiled and, as the tubuli recti, lead to the rete cords, which are merely the central ends of the original ingrowths and form their own irregular net in the mediastinum. All the cords remain solid until shortly before puberty.

Meanwhile, the ovary lags somewhat in differentiation. The primary cell cords from the mesothelium remain as an ill-defined group, containing sex cells and undifferentiated cells, and become separated from the mesothelial surface by a wide band of mesenchyma called the capsule, the periphery of which makes a lesser tunica albuginea. From the third to the fifth fetal month a renewed activity of the mesothelium sends into this capsule a new homogeneous mass of cells, the cortex; in other mammals this invasion is in the form of individual cords—Pflüger's egg-tubes—but in man no cords are evident. Later the new mass is divided by mesenchyma into small nests of cells, called follicles, each containing one or more primary sex cells, called oögonia. Whether these true oögonia are derived by the migration of some of the original sex cells of the inner mass into the cortex, or by the ingrowth of new elements with the new cortical material is not known. Most of the sex cells of the inner mass degenerate, while the original cords serve as the rete cords of the ovarian medulla.

Between the cords of the testis and around the cell nests of the ovary, during the fourth month of development, masses of large epithelioid cells appear in the mesenchyma; these are the interstitial cells, believed to produce the sex hormones. In the testis they are more conspicuous and appear earlier than in the ovary, and in

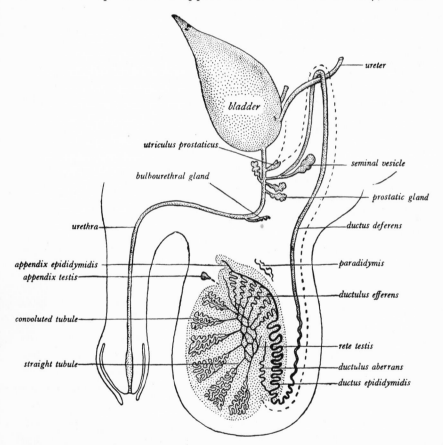

Fig. 59. Diagram of the male sexual organs. (The course of the paramesonephric duct is indicated by dashes.) [From J. L. Bremer and H. L. Weatherford, *Textbook of histology* (Blakiston Div., McGraw-Hill, New York, ed. 6, 1944).]

the male, strangely enough, they are more numerous at their first appearance than later on. Their origin is unknown.

The relation of the sex gland to the mesonephros differs radically in the two sexes. The greater number of the mesonephric tubules have already degenerated by the third month (p. 88), but from 10 to 15 of the more cranial ones remain intact, though inactive. In the male the rete cords of the testis make connection with this upper group of mesonephric nephrons, either by the glomerular capsule or by one of the neighboring tubular convolutions (Fig. 58), and when the testis cords become tubular this group serves as the outlet for the genital products to the mesonephric duct, and are known as the vasa efferentia or ductuli efferentes. Both the vasa and the associated portion of the mesonephric duct increase greatly in length and coil tightly on themselves to form the head of the epididymis, each vas forming a lobule; the lower part of the duct within the mesonephros also coils and makes the body and tail of the epididymis (Fig. 59). Other fragmented tubules remain inactive as the paradidymis. The terminal free portion of the mesonephric duct, that not included within the limits of the gland itself, becomes the ductus deferens, and, beyond the outgrowing seminal vesicle, is known as the ductus ejaculatorius. The prostate gland, on the other hand, develops from the urethra. Its 50 to 70 individual outgrowths [11] from all sides of the urethra are grouped in five lobes, of which the anterior pair show such distinctive characteristics as to suggest for them an individual function. The cranial end of the mesonephric duct may be preserved as the inconstant appendix epididymidis. The appendix testis is the upper end of the paramesonephric duct.

In the female the rete cords of the ovary make no connection with the mesonephric tubules, which all degenerate completely, except for vestigial upper and lower groups forming the epoöphoron and paroöphoron respectively (Fig. 55). The mesonephric ducts also disappear for most of their length, each being represented only by the ovarian hydatid or appendix vesiculosa cranially and by the inconstant Gartner's canal in the uterine wall distally. Before puberty the cell nests in the ovarian cortex develop into follicles, some of which from time to time become vesicular; with each menstruation one or more of the vesicular follicles enlarges, breaks through the tunica albuginea and the ovarian mesothelium, and ruptures, casting the enclosed ovum or ova into the peritoneal cavity. The entrance of the ripe ovum into the uterine tube is not left entirely to chance, however; it is aided by the active peristalsis [12] of the whole length of the usually inactive tube and by violent sweeping motions of the fimbriae. This periodic activity is induced by the presence of the hormone contained in the liquor folliculi and released at ovulation. Ciliary action within the tube is also intensified, helping to move the ovum, once captured, down to the uterus. In the absence of spermatozoa the ovum degenerates and is lost during menstruation, while the uterine tube returns to its inactive state. The voluminous folds of its mucosa normally close it effectively, but the potentially uninterrupted passage from vagina to abdominal cavity opens a possible path for bacteria to the tube or even to the peritoneal cavity.

In the event of insemination the spermatozoa usually meet the ovum in the upper part, or ampulla, of the tube. If fertilization takes place the ovum normally passes on to the uterus and there makes a placental connection with the uterine mucosa for further growth. The abnormal failure of the ovum to reach the uterus results in ectopic or extrauterine pregnancy, terms which apply to either the tubal or the abdominal type. In tubal pregnancy the fertilized ovum is retained in the tube, either because of tubal stenosis or by being caught in a pocket formed by a chance fusion of the mucosal folds. Placental connections may be made with the wall of the tube and growth may progress until the enlarging embryo ruptures the tubal wall (usually at about 6 weeks) calling for operative interference. Abdominal pregnancy occurs much more rarely, either as the result of the extrusion of the fertilized ovum from the mouth of the tube or through an early rupture of the tubal wall, which subsequently heals after expulsion of the ovum. Fertilization within the abdominal cavity probably does not occur. Usually the extruded fertilized ovum dies and is absorbed, but occasionally it may find a placental attachment on the sigmoid or colon or on their mesenteries, or on some other abdominal organ, and grow to a considerable size. When not removed surgically it may either be resorbed or become calcified (lithopedion).[13] Ovarian pregnancy has been reported, but also doubted.[14] Only the early segmentation of the ovum is described in these reports, and this may well represent the initial stage of a dermoid cyst of the ovary or of its solid counter-part, an ovarian teratoma. The rare finding of an island of uterine mucosa in the ovarian cortex has been explained as probably due to the former presence of an accessory paramesonephric duct, its distal end entrapped within the genital gland and there transformed into uterine tissue, in the normal manner but in the wrong position (p. 104).

As the mesonephric tubules degenerate from above downward, the genital glands of both sexes descend to the pelvic rim, attached to the dorsal wall by the remaining connective tissue of the mesonephric ridge which thus forms a short mesorchium or mesovarium. The same field of connective tissue supports also the appropriate persisting duct, mesonephric in the male, paramesonephric in the female, but with differing relations. In the male the mesonephric duct follows the testis in its further descent into the scrotum. The mesorchium is occupied by the epididymis. In the female, as the paramesonephric ducts turn mesially to form the uterus, each duct carries with it the peritoneal layer in which it lies, which is thus stretched until it resembles a broad sheet hung over a clothesline. This double sheet is called the broad ligament in the uterine portion, the mesosalpynx where it is supported by the uterine tube. In this process the ovary is lifted also, between the two layers of the mesosalpynx, but projecting from the dorsal sheet on its own short mesovarium. The broad ligaments of the two sides, with the uterus between them, form a partition dividing the female pelvis into the rectouterine fossa dorsally (the pouch of Douglas) and the lesser vesiculouterine fossa ventrally. Within the broad ligament a thickened strand, the round ligament, runs from each upper lateral corner of the uterus to the ventral body wall where it is attached to the musculature in the region of the labia majora. A second, less conspicuous strand, the ovarian ligament, passes from the uterus to the ovary through the mesosalpynx.

Descent of the testis. In the male each testis, with its accompanying epididymis, remains close to the dorsal wall, supported by the short mesorchium, which represents the mesoderm of the much reduced mesonephric ridge. A continuation of this ridge beyond the caudal limit of the mesonephros runs on each side as a prominent retroperitoneal cord to the ventral body wall, following the curve of the pelvic cavity, which at this time is merely a shallow bay. In the ventral wall it is attached to the musculature of the genital swelling or scrotum. This cord is the gubernaculum testis. It is not, as often stated, the counterpart of the round ligament in the female, for the gubernaculum testis connects the ventral body wall with the sex gland directly, while the round ligament connects this wall with the uterus. To complete the male gubernaculum one must add to the round ligament the ovarian ligament, from uterus to ovary. In both round ligament and gubernaculum a few strands of smooth muscle develop in late fetal life.

At about the third month a small area of the body wall on each side, including the attachment of the gubernaculum or of the round ligament, bulges forward or outward, carrying with it the corresponding layer of the peritoneum (Fig. 60, *A*). In the female the resulting external bilateral mounds form the labia majora; in the male the two mounds fuse as the scrotum. The internal peritoneal sac in each prominence is the processus vaginalis, around the mouth of which the tissues of the body wall form the ligaments that mark the inguinal canal. In the female the processus remains small, usually present in infancy as a funnel-shaped depression partially surrounding the insertion of the round ligament and known as the canal of Nuck; later it is often completely obliterated. In the male both the scrotum and the paired peritoneal protrusions within it enlarge progressively.

From the sixth to the ninth fetal month the gubernaculum testis lengthens more slowly than the body wall against which it rests, and as the result of this unequal growth rate the testis and epididymis are drawn to the dorsal wall of the internal inguinal ring (Fig. 60, *B*). At about the time of birth, but with wide individual variation, the growth of the gubernaculum ceases entirely or is succeeded by a certain degree of shortening, perhaps aided by the contraction of its newly acquired muscles, and the testis is thereby drawn within and through the inguinal canal into the scrotum, which enlarges to receive it (Fig. 60, *C*). During its course it remains retroperitoneal, and in the scrotum it still retains this condition, being invested by a visceral layer of the processus vaginalis. The cavity of the processus or tunica vaginalis, as it is now called, is thus reduced to a slit, crescentic in section, with little space be-

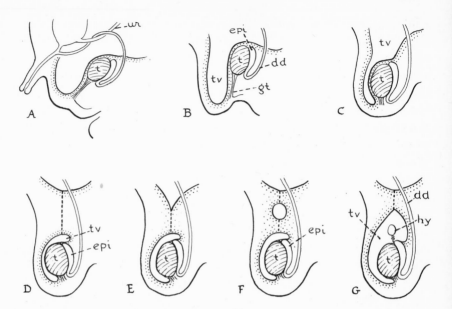

Fig. 60. Diagrams showing descent of testis into scrotum. *dd.,* ductus deferens; *epi,* epididymis; *gt,* gubernaculum testis; *hy,* hydatid; *t,* testis; *tv,* tunica vaginalis; *ur,* ureter.

tween visceral and parietal layers. The neck of the processus then becomes obliterated (Fig. 60, *D*). This is the normal sequence of events, but in certain cases one or both testes may remain in the pelvic cavity until puberty and then either descend properly or become fixed in that pelvic position by adhesions. This condition is known as cryptorchism. In other cases the testis may remain in the inguinal canal, drawn there by cremasteric spasm (retracted testis), in which position it is almost always accompanied by an indirect inguinal hernia. More rarely, if the internal peritoneal sac does not coincide in location with the attachment of the gubernaculum, the testis may not reach the vaginal process, but pass lateral to it into the subcutaneous tissue of the thigh or of the ventral body wall; this condition is known as ectopia testis.

The descent of the testis is an essentially male sequence, yet a comparable shortening of the ligament attached to the ventral body wall is present also in the female. After birth the round ligament ceases to grow as fast as the surrounding parts, with the result that the position of the uterus is changed from the vertically upright condition of infancy to the slight anteflexion of older life. Moreover, as a very rare anomaly,[15] the round ligament and ovarian ligament of one side may retract as a unit in late fetal life and cause the descent, not only of the ovary, but of the uterine tube and part of the uterus as well into the much distended canal of Nuck, nearly obliterating the broad ligament and enlarging tremendously the labium majus. Since the descent of the male gonad is due to the presence of the male hormone,[16] it is probable that the cause of this female quasi-descent is some form of hormonal imbalance.

The processus vaginalis lends itself readily to several types of disorders. The neck, i.e., the passage from the pelvic cavity to the scrotal sac, normally closes after the descent of the testis at about birth; if it remains open it offers the opportunity for congenital inguinal hernia. The closure may take place irregularly, leaving small closed cysts along its course (Fig. 60, *F*), which may enlarge as cysts of the spermatic cord. After closure the lining cells of the scrotal sac may abnormally secrete an excess of fluid, with resulting hydrocele (*G*).

External genitalia. The development of the external genitalia in the two sexes and the explanation of the various anomalies that may occur in their formation are intimately related to the history of the cloacal membrane. This membrane or plate is first seen in the young flat embryo as a narrow median-line structure extending caudally from the primitive streak to the base of the body stalk (Fig. 61, *a*); along its length the ectoderm of the future skin and the entoderm of the yolk sac are fused, with no mesoderm between them. With the growth of the embryo and the rolling under of the body stalk to form its part of the umbilical cord, the primarily caudal end of the cloacal membrane is carried to the ventral abdominal wall (*b, c*), while its formerly cranial end lies near the base of the tail; in this position the membrane forms the caudal and ventral walls of the laterally compressed cloaca. It is no sooner established along its full length than it is interrupted by the formation of the perineum (p. 69), which divides it into an anal membrane caudally and a urogenital membrane ventrally, the latter bounding the urogenital sinus. It is this latter ventral portion, and the growth of the mesodermal tissues bounding it, that determine the form of the external genitalia.

Even before the perineal ridges have completed the division of the cloaca, the body-wall masses of which the longitudinal ridges are a part continue their ventral extension on each side to form the muscles and fasciae of the ventral abdominal wall, aided by other mesoderm from the caudal wall of the umbilical cord.[17] The abdominal wall is thus expanded both horizontally and vertically (Fig. 25), and as the cells from the various sources meet in the midline they split the ventral portion of the urogenital membrane into its two components, the ectoderm for the skin and the entoderm for the ventral wall of the urogenital sinus, which latter soon becomes divided into the vesicular bladder above and the constricted membranous urethra below (Fig. 61, *g, f*). The urogenital membrane is

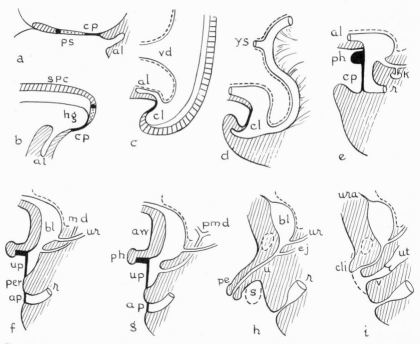

Fig. 61. Diagrams to explain successive division, shortening, and final disappearance of the cloacal membrane (plate) and its relation to the urogenital organs in both sexes. Cloacal plate designated by heavy line. (*f*) and (*h*) depict conditions in male; (*g*) and (*i*) in female. *al*, allantois; *ap*, anal plate; *aw*, abdominal wall; *bl*, badder; *cl*, cloaca; *cli*, clitoris; *cp*, cloacal plate; *ej*, ejaculatory duct; *hg*, hindgut; *k*, kidney; *md*, mesonephric duct; *pe*, penis; *per*, perineum; *ph*, phallus; *pmd*, paramesonephric duct; *ps*, primitive streak; *r*, rectum; *s*, scrotum; *spc*, spinal cord; *u*, urethra; *ur*, ureter; *up*, urogenital plate; *ura*, urachus; *ut*, uterus; *v*, vagina; *vd*, vitelline duct; *ys*, yolk stalk.

thereby made relatively shorter, and at the point where the remaining membrane and the new body wall meet a rounded, primarily
paired eminence develops, called the genital tubercle or phallus.
The cranial half of this mound is an extension of the body wall,
with mesoderm separating the ectoderm and entoderm, but along
the caudal mid-line mesenchyma is absent and the urogenital membrane is drawn out as a median septum or keel of combined ectoderm and entoderm, the phallic plate, its upper border continuing
the line of the upper wall of the reduced urogenital sinus. The
genital tubercle is to become the penis in the male or the clitoris in
the female.

On either side of the shortened urogenital membrane and
around the genital tubercle, paired surface ridges appear during
the seventh week, forming between them a deep groove at the bottom of which the membrane lies. They form between or within the
two labioscrotal folds and are called the urethral folds, destined to
remain separated in the female as the labia minora, while in the
male they unite progressively forward from the perineum, obliterating the caudal portion of the urogenital sinus within.

The genital tubercle, meanwhile, in both sexes grows longer
and develops at its tip the globular glans, the base of which is
marked by a slight groove. The deep border of the median septum
of the phallus grows into the glans secondarily and projects from its
tip as an epithelial tag. The subsequent routine now differs in the
two sexes. In the male the median septum in the phallus splits
sagitally, forming a deep V-shaped trough, the edges of which later
close over and fuse to produce the tubelike penile urethra, continuing the male membranous urethra within the body; in the female
the septum and epithelial tag are present for a short time, but no
groove is formed and soon both the tag and the whole length of the
original septum disappear. The prepuce develops in both sexes by
the ingrowth, from the front of the glans backward, of a collar of
surface epithelium incomplete on the perineal side. The central
cells degenerate and free a double-layered sleeve covering the glans,
held ventrally by the frenulum.

The surface changes in the external genitalia can best be followed in a series of photographs of embryos of known ages, such
as those given by Spaulding[18] and others, as found in the many

textbooks of embryology. The chief distinguishing characteristics are the length of the urethral folds and their relation to the lateral swellings, the greater length and erectness of the phallus in the male, and the earlier formation of the glans in the female. But these criteria are by no means convincing in the early fetal months.

The anomalies of the external cloacal region are connected with the fate of the cloacal membrane and the urethral folds and, as usual, the terminal events of the sequence are the most liable to be at fault. The closure of the urethral folds is a male characteristic and hence the more common anomalies are found in the male as the result of irregularities in this closure, causing the various types of hypospadias, in which the urethra opens on the under surface of the penis (Fig. 62, *c*). The opening may be near the glans, along the whole penis, or near its base; these are obviously cases of arrested development, since they closely resemble the conditions found in normal fetuses. The urethral meatus may even be situated along the scrotal raphé, in which case the phallic plate is not implicated, but merely the urogenital membrane below it (*d*). The extensive forms of these conditions are the basis of false hermaphrodism, for if the urethral meatus extends as a sagittal slit for some distance along the raphé, the two scrotal mounds may resemble closely the labia majora, the urethral cavity between them appearing as the vulva. Careful examination can usually establish the sex, but the final proof lies in the operative examination of the gonads.

The rarer anomalies include epispadias and exstrophy of the bladder. These conditions are due to the retention and later rupture of some part of the urogenital membrane above its normal level, or, in other words, to the local failure of the lateral mesodermal masses to reach the mid-line in some region above the center of the genital tubercle. Differently expressed, the tubercle is formed too far caudally.[19] Around this supraphallic urogenital membrane no urethral folds develop; in extent it may be limited to the penis, where it is represented by the presence of the phallic plate along the dorsal instead of the normal ventral half of the tubercle, or it may include the whole length of the abdominal wall as far as the umbilicus, or be present on any portion of this length. In the penis this position of the phallic plate may lead to the various forms of epispadias (Fig. 62, *b*); along the mid-ventral abdom-

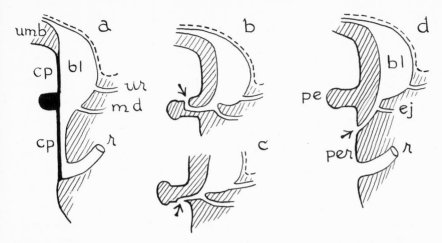

Fig. 62. Diagrams to explain (b) epispadias, (c) hypospadias, and (d) perineal urethral meatus as abnormal local persistence and later rupture of unusual portions of the cloacal plate; more extensive retention of the plate may lead to exstrophy of the bladder. Lettering as in Fig. 61.

inal wall the rupture of the urogenital membrane where it has failed to be reinforced by mesoderm results in extrophy of the bladder, ectopia vesicae.

In epispadias, as in hypospadias, the urethral meatus may be of normal size and situated at any point between the base of the penis and the tip of the glans, or it may be in the form of a long cleft along much or all of this distance. The anomalous opening may be an accessory meatus for a urethra of normal length, or it may be the only meatus of a shortened urethra, and, if situated at the base of the penis, among the suprapubic folds, it may escape notice for several weeks after birth. In a very rare type of epispadias the accessory orifice is the mouth of a separate, accessory urethra,[20] leading from the ventral bladder wall, without spinchter, to its meatus at the base of the penis (Fig. 63), or even to the end of the glans. In one such case recently seen in this hospital the accessory urethra was incomplete and ended blindly in the body wall, not connected with the bladder. The great majority of those reported pass beneath the symphysis pubis, but a very few have been above it. To account for these accessory urethras, one must postulate the former presence of an irregular groove on the surface of one or both

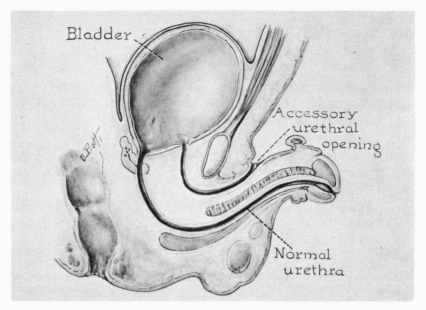

Fig. 63. Drawing of epispadias and accessory ureter. [From Gross and Moore, *Arch. Surg.* 60, 751 (1950).]

of the advancing masses of lateral mesoderm, resulting in a tubular remnant of the original genitourinary sinus, traversing all or most of the newly made ventral wall, with rupture of the closing membrane. The principle is the same as in rectoperineal fistula, and such an accessory urethra might well be called a vesico-abdominal fistula.

Exstrophy of the bladder may be of several grades and appear in either sex. The defect commonly occupies the lower abdominal wall and shows the openings of the two ureters and the single urethra; or this type may be associated with epispadias, the open ventral cleft being continuous from abdomen to penis. On the other hand, the exstrophy may reach nearly to the umbilicus, laying open part of the normal urachus, or it may be continued caudally to the perineum. In this last type the symphysis pubis is absent, the distinction between bladder and urethra is lost, and the phallic tubercle is split, its two original halves lying at either side at the skin-mucosa junction, and either the whole vulva is laid open or the scrotal sac is split and reduced to lateral mounds, for cryptorchism is the rule in such cases. The still more extreme condition, in which the rectum is included in the exstrophy through complete absence of the perineum, is very rare. The greater part of the cloacal plate is affected, the rectum and the ureters, devoid of sphyncters, open directly to the surface, along with either the ejaculatory ducts or the vagina, according to sex. One such case seen by me was complicated by the intussusception of the rectum which protruded stiffly in the median line, grossly suggesting a penis, but readily recognized on closer examination; the two halves of the phallus were present laterally, situated on either side at the skin-mucosal junction.

In direct contrast to the extreme degrees of exstrophy, in which the extended cloacal plate ruptures and exposes the whole cloaca, are the rare cloacal cysts caused by the permanent retention and reinforcement of the entire cloacal plate, permitting no outlet for either the intestinal or genitourinary system. The result is similar to hydrocolpos on a grand scale (p. 107). The abdomen is enormously distended and the external genitalia inhibited and stretched almost beyond recognition. Such anomalous fetuses have been delivered either suprapubicly or after withdrawal of the fluid by puncture, but can hardly be considered viable; others have succumbed in utero to the failure of the heart from pressure of the cyst.

8 ——

HEART, I

The embryo, during the early days while the germ layers are being formed, derives its nutriment by imbibition from the fluids in which it floats and by absorption of the yolk granules contained in the mature ovum. When the germ layers become differentiated, this yolk material is segregated in the entodermal cells of the yolk sac, and thence is transferred from cell to cell throughout the embryo. In birds the large store of yolk is practically the only source of nutriment until the chick is hatched, and when the yolk granules in the entodermal cells near the axis of the embryo are exhausted, so that the cell-to-cell method of transfer is no longer adequate, the earliest blood vessels and blood corpuscles are formed to provide a new method of transportation. The vessels first appear in close relation with the more distal, still yolk-laden entodermal cells and grow toward the axis of the embryo, and the yolk material in solution is transferred to the blood in the vessels distally and given up again to the body cells. In man also the blood vessels develop on the yolk sac and grow toward the embryonic body, but the human yolk is strictly limited, and a new source of food is soon provided by the implantation of the ovum and the formation of the placenta. In this organ a second set of blood vessels is formed,[1] appearing at first in close relation with the maternal blood, and growing along the body stalk, where new vascular links are added;[2] food and oxygen are taken from the maternal blood by the fluid and corpuscles within the embryonic vessels and distributed to the embryonic body. This supply is inexhaustible and only terminated at birth. The yolk-sac system of vessels is called vitelline (*vitellus* = yolk in Latin) and its branches serve the yolk-sac derivatives, i.e., the different parts of the alimentary tract. The vessels from the placenta are the umbilical vessels, for the body stalk in which they run is an essential part of the umbilical cord; they are also known as the allantoic vessels, since they accompany the allantois in the body stalk. These original vessels are thus extraembryonic in origin and also venous in function, their blood flowing toward the center of the embryo. To complete the circulation outgoing vessels are also necessary, vessels arterial in function, in which the blood flows toward the stores of food, and connected with the veins both centrally and peripherally. The early embryologists taught that these arterial vessels, as well as all the venous trunks of the body, developed as extensions of the plexus on the yolk sac, but in the early years of this century a group of anatomists rejected this idea and maintained that blood vessels develop in situ in many regions of the body, by the vacuolization of mesenchymal cells or by the rearrangement and flattening of these cells as walls around former intercellular spaces, thereby forming isolated cysts (*angiocysts*), and that chains of these cysts later anastomose to produce intraembryonic trunks, at first plexiform. Now it is generally conceded that angiogenesis (i.e., the formation of blood vessels) does take place within the body, but it is primarily restricted to a linear region on each side of the neural groove between the somites and the underlying entoderm. From these limited centers develop the originally paired aortae, the source of all arterial trunks of the body, which in turn send branches to join the yolk-sac and placental plexuses (Figs. 64 and 65).

The mammalian heart develops in the cephalic end of the body during the first days of the fourth week of embryonic life. In most mammals it is originally double; each half-heart lies near the median wall of the coelom and represents the conjoined mesial ends of all the vitelline veins from that side of the yolk sac. Soon these members of the vitelline plexus are reduced to a single vein, entering the caudal end of a longitudinal vessel, the half-heart proper. Like all vitelline vessels, the heart lies between the entoderm of the yolk sac and the adjoining splanchnic mesoderm, and as it grows larger it bulges the mesodermal sheet overlying it and thus becomes double-layered in most of its circumference, endothelium

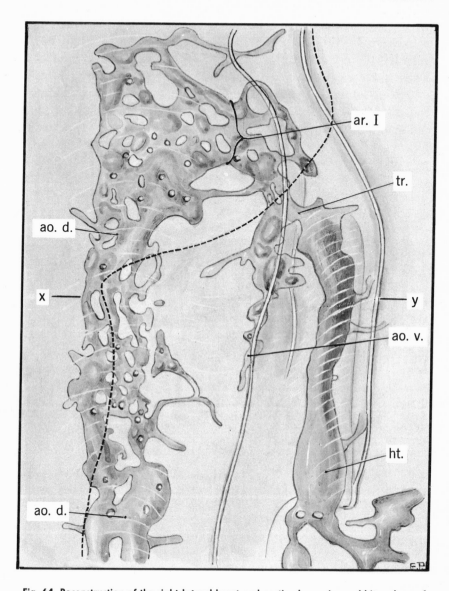

Fig. 64. Reconstruction of the right lateral heart and aortic plexus, in a rabbit embryo of 8½ days, dorsal view. The heart (*ht*) extends as a straight tube from the entering veins caudally to the truncus arteriosus (*tr.*), by which it is connected with the first aortic arch (*ar.I.*) and the ventral aorta (*ao.v.*). The aortic arch and the dorsal aorta (*ao.d.*) are both plexiform. Double line indicates the cut edge of the coelomic somatopleure; broken line, lateral limit of overlying neural groove and optic vesicle. *x-y*, position of section in Fig. 65. [From original of Fig. 3, J. L. Bremer, *Am. J. Anat., 13*, 118 (1912).]

within and mesoderm fitting loosely over it (Fig. 65). Since the mesodermal layer is to form both heart muscle and epicardium, it is called the epimyocardium. With the folding off of the growing head above the floor of the amniotic cavity, the lateral embryonic layers, carrying the two lateral hearts in their separate coeloms, are rolled under and meet, the most mesial portions of the splanchnopleures forming the floor of the foregut, the next lateral portions fusing and dissolving, so that the two endothelial half-hearts may join as a single tube. The now single heart is double-walled, inverted, and suspended from the floor of the foregut by the dorsal mesocardium. The somatopleure of the now fused lateral coeloms makes part of the chest wall.

Figures 64 and 65 are from the rabbit,[3] an animal in which heart formation is definitely lateral. In the human embryo yolk-sac angiogenesis is minimal and even before the resulting capillaries can grow to the median coelomic area, another site for vessel formation is provided by the development from the lateral coeloms of two mesial intraembryonic branches, running as narrow tubular coelomic extensions forward on either side of the future head and meeting in front of it across the median line,[4] yet separated from it by a narrow strip in which mesoderm is absent (Fig. 66, *A*); in this strip the remaining ectoderm and entoderm form a plate, the forerunner of the oral membrane medially and of the closing plates of the branchial pouches laterally.

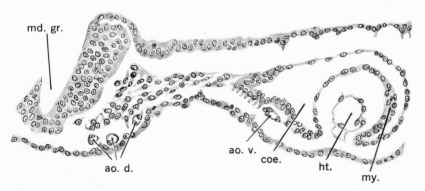

md. gr.

ao. v.

coe.

ht.

my.

ao. d.

Fig. 65. Section through plane x-y in Fig. 64. *ao.d., ao.v.,* dorsal and ventral aortae; *coe.,* coelom; *ht.,* heart; *md.gr.,* medullary groove; *my.,* epimyocardium. [From original of Fig. 4, J. L. Bremer, Am. J. Anat. *13,* 119 (1912).]

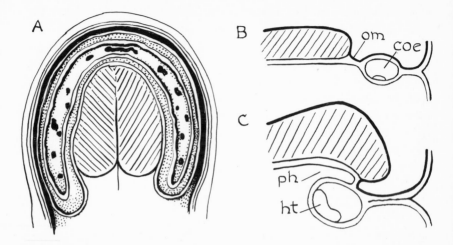

Fig. 66. (A) Dorsal view of head end of late presomite human embryo. Medullary plates indicated by diagonal lines; closely surrounding these are oral and gill-pouch membrane (stippled), extension of coelom with angioblasts, and the fetal membranes. (After Davis.) (B) Median sagittal section of (A); (C) result of forward growth of head. coe, coelom with angioblast; ht, heart; om, oral membrane (plate); ph, pharynx.

In the splanchnopleure of this horseshoe-shaped coelomic extension the human heart develops by the growth and later union of many individual new centers of angiogenesis; and, as the neural plates grow longer and override the floor of the amniotic cavity to form the free head, the transverse portion of the tubular coelom with its developing vessels is inverted and rolled under from the front (Fig. 66, *B, C*). The simultaneous lifting of the head rolls the lateral portions under from the sides, as in the rabbit heart. That the folding takes place in both directions is shown by many drawings of the endothelial outline of young human hearts, showing the cranial portion as a single tube, the caudal part still composed of two lateral mambers. In either case, whether the two half-hearts are rolled under from the sides and then unite, as in most mammals, or the already united median angiocysts are folded under the head from in front as well as from the sides, as in man, the result is a single inverted median structure, which soon meets and joins the cranial ends of the two aortic plexuses around the front of the pharynx, as the first aortic arches, and caudally is connected with the vitelline and umbilical veins. The vitelline veins, originally entering each half-heart from the side, have in the formation of the caudal end of the heart been rolled under the foregut and now lie nearer the median line and pierce the septum transversum; the umbilical veins, running in the body wall and there joining the common cardinal veins collecting the blood from head and trunk, take a somewhat more lateral position within the septum. These three venous trunks from each side combine to form the right and left horns of the sinus venosus, which opens into the atrial end of the heart by a single median mouth.

A sagittal view of the heart in this condition (Fig. 67, *D*) shows a double-walled tube ventral to the foregut, joined by the veins caudally and continuing cranially to the paired first aortic arches. The heart lies in a constricted medial part of the coelom, limited cranially by the chest wall caudal to the head, and caudally by the septum transversum. The chest wall and the septum are relatively stable structures, and as the heart tube grows rapidly in length between these fixed points it responds by bending sinuously, to the left caudally, to the right cranially (*E*), as though crumpled on itself.

It is probably at this time that the intrinsic activity of the human heart begins. In the chick[5] this activity can be studied directly through a hole made in the shell, or the living embryo can be removed from the yolk and observed by reflected light from time to time for several hours while development of the heart progresses. For a true understanding, therefore, of the developmental processes involved in the early development of the tubular heart it is well to study avian forms, even though the mammalian heart has now also been similarly studied.[6]

In the chick, then, the heart beat is first seen when the embryo is in the condition of slight right-left flexure, as shown in Figure 67, *E*, representing about 48 hours incubation in the chick, the end of the third week in man. Histological examination of similar embryos shows that at this stage of development the cells of the epimyocardium show only a few immature myofibrils and no other recognizable differentiation commonly found in muscle cells, and that they have no connection with any nerves.[7] The activity is initiated by an irregular, intermittent twitching of the dextral sur-

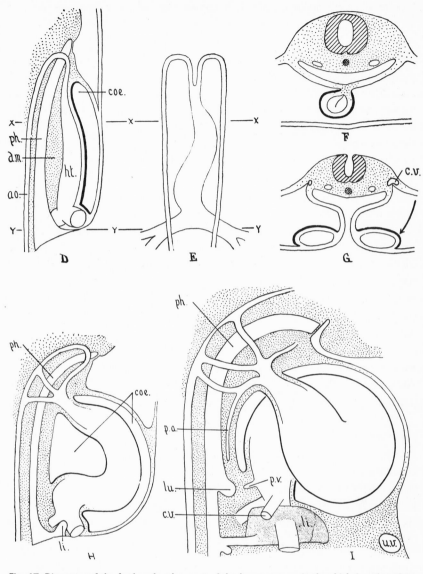

Fig. 67. Diagrams of the further development of the heart as seen in the chick (continuation of Fig. 66): (D) sagittal and (E) dorsal views of chick of about 10 somites; (F) and (G) cross sections of same embryo along lines x-y and y-y; (H) and (I) successively older embryos. ao., aorta; coe., coelom; c.v., common cardinal vein; d.m., dorsal mesocardium; ht., heart; li., liver; lu., lung bud; p.a., p.v., pulmonary artery and vein; ph., pharynx; u.v., umbilical vein. [From J. L. Bremer and H. L. Weatherford, Textbook of histology (Blakiston Div., McGraw-Hill, New York, ed. 6, 1944).]

face of the cranial bend of the heart, a part of the tube that later is to become right ventricle. The twitching slowly changes to peristaltic waves of contraction from this point forward toward the aortic trunk, the remaining caudal portion of the heart being as yet motionless. Then the starting point of the peristalsis moves caudally until the whole heart is in motion, each wave beginning at the caudal end, and even on the entering veins, and sweeping forward. The whole sequence, from the first twitching motion to the peristalsis of the whole tube, occupies only 1 or 2 hours and is so distinct that it has been reproduced, in part, in motion pictures. There can be little doubt that the initiation of heart activity in the human embryo follows a somewhat similar pattern; it has already been noted in the rat.[8]

For a while the action is purely peristaltic, but soon some kind of valve is needed to prevent the return, between contractions, of blood from the nonperistaltic and inert aortae beyond. This need is supplied by two small thickenings or cushions of modified subendothelial gel situated on the opposing cranial and caudal walls of the tube at the cranial end of the heart, just within the pericardial cavity, which are brought together at the end of each successive contraction, thus effectively closing the lumen to return flow, and only separate again as the next contraction wave approaches. As soon as the aortic trunk acquires its own muscular coat these primary valves disappear.

The early right-left orientation of the crumpled heart tube is constant, except in a few anomalous instances. Its cause is not clear. It has been stated that in the early fusion of the two lateral hearts, in animals like the cat or the rabbit in which the lateral motion predominates, the right member supplies the greater share cranially, the left member caudally, so that the two bends are inherent; but this only leads to a further question as to why this type of asymmetry is so constant, to which we have no answer.

Meanwhile, further lengthening of the heart tube increases the sweep of the two bends, to left and to right, until the craniocaudally compressed heart resembles an inverted letter S, carrying the formerly median mouth of the sinus venosus farther to the right; the left horn of the sinus thus becomes longer than the right, and the sinus mouth into the atrium is drawn to a transverse oval shape.

Continued lengthening forces the heart tube into a deep sagittal curve (Fig. 67, *H*), so deep that the dorsal mesocardium is stretched and ruptured, except in its most caudal portion where the future atria are to develop, and the tube thus becomes almost completely double-walled, attached at its two ends but otherwise free in the pericardial cavity. This rupture of the dorsal mesocardium produces the transverse sinus of the adult heart. The free part of the curved heart then changes to a loop or ring form (Fig. 67, *I*), the natural result of further lengthening. Similar changes can be followed by bringing the two ends of a short length of rubber tubing closer together (Fig. 68), thus imitating the relative lengthening of the tube within a confined space, and, as the cranial end of the heart tube already bends to the right, it now passes close to the right of the caudal, or atrial, end. The coil thus forms a sinistral spiral, which, since the two ends of the tube are fixed, must be neutralized by a dextral twist or spiral along the length of the tube itself. If from a roll or spool of ribbon a single coil is drawn from one end, not unrolled in the usual way, the spiral action of the coil will be evident. In the developing heart the dextral spiral is normal, and it is recognizable in the adult heart in the winding of the aorta and pulmonary trunk about each other, also in a dextral spiral.

In the chick, while the young heart tube is in the loop form (Fig. 67, *I*) the bulging right wall of the common atrium overlaps the ascending limb of the ventricle, and with each peristaltic heart beat this right side of the atrium is lifted dorsally, until, with continued growth, the atrium as a whole is tilted transversely, its right side more dorsal than the left. In consequence, the veins entering from the left tend to be directed ventrally, those from the right dorsally; the blood from the right side of the body will pass through the center of the atrium diagonally forward (cranially) and to the left, following the primary left curvature of the atrial end of the heart tube (Fig. 67, *E*) to enter the atrioventricular canal, while that from the left, directed ventrally, will run along the floor of the atrium forward and toward the right atrial wall. Thus the asymmetry of the atrium, due to simple mechanical causes, leads to the production of two individual streams of blood within the young heart, the differing courses of which are to determine the location of certain of the heart septa soon to be formed.

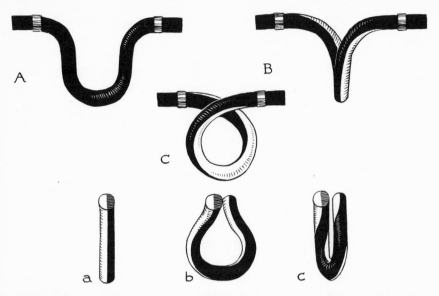

Fig. 68. Drawings. of rubber tube held rigidly by clamps at either end showing formation of dextral spiral as the tube is forced into shapes simulating those of the developing heart. Lateral and caudal views. [From original of Fig. 4, J. L. Bremer, *Anat. Rec. 37*, 233 (1928).]

The propulsive force for the two streams is provided by the waves of peristaltic contraction, beginning in the veins and transmitted first to the right atrial wall, as the next cranial segment of the tube, and thence to the left atrial wall, and so to the atrioventricular canal and the ventricles. Each pulsation consists of a sharp, rapid contraction and an immediate equally rapid recovery, followed by a considerable wait before the next beat. The stream from the left vein, running along the atrial floor, is thus met by the hammer stroke of the curved right atrial wall, beating toward the median line. This would have the same effect as when a spoon, concave face forward and with only the lower edge immersed, is flicked rapidly through the water in a bowl; a thin jet of surface water, after following the concavity of the spoon, spurts forward from its upper lip in the direction of the force applied. In the heart the blood would be spurted along the roof of the atrial cavity toward the left wall, there to be met a second time by the rapid opposing beat of the rounded left atrial wall, which, because it slants somewhat cranially, deflects the stream down the left wall of the atrioventricular canal. The accurately timed, successive contractions of the left vein, right atrial wall, and left atrial wall thus provide sufficient force to give to the left stream a continued or even accelerated speed, and the shape of the tilted atrium causes it to flow in a sinistral spiral partly around the current from the right vein, as the latter passes through the atrium to the canal. The right and left walls of the common atrium, since they play the chief part in the deflection of the left stream, bulge laterally still farther as the right and left atria, apparently side by side in the fetal and adult heart but actually in tandem formation along the sinuously bent embryonic heart tube.

These facts were elicited [9] by the study of the heart in chick embryos in which the head normally turns to the right and lies on its left side at the critical period. It might well be thought that this torsion of the embryo alone is a sufficient cause for the asymmetrical position of the two entering veins, but in those few abnormal chick embryos in which the head turns to the left, instead of to the right (heterotaxis), and in other chicks in which the position of the head has been previously forcibly reversed, the relative position of the veins is the same as in the normal embryo, showing that the cause is intrinsic in the shape of the coiled heart itself, and that the knowledge gained from the readily visible avian heart may perhaps be safely applied to other coiled hearts not available for direct study in the living condition. Only in the living animal, with the circulation intact, is the ever-changing shape of the beating heart normal; any manipulation of the embryo may distort the delicate atrial walls. The drawing (Fig. 69, A) shows a model made from serial sections of the atrium and part of the ventricular loop of a chick heart in the tightly coiled stage, viewed from the caudal end of the body, looking forward. The thin-walled atrial roof has obviously collapsed during fixation of the embryo. The model shows the ascending limb of the ventricle (a.l.v.) in position to lift the right wall of the atrium, and the relation of the atrium as a whole to the anterior intestinal portal. The courses of the two blood streams, from right and left, are indicated. The next drawing (B) is of a hollow glass model blown in the observed true shape of the living atrium of the chick of this age, with right and left entrance tubes pointing in the known direction of the entering veins, and a larger exit, representing the

atrioventricular canal. A swift stream of water through the left entrance tube follows the course indicated by the flock of arrows,
along the atrial floor to the right wall, to the roof, to the left wall,
and then down the canal.

The two streams in the atria can be studied directly in the living chick, and even viewed from several angles, for with each
pulsation a group of blood corpuscles from each vein comes into
view as a definitely outlined dark shadow which can be followed in its
future course. The two separate courses can even be recorded by
use of the motion-picture camera, for the strips of photographs,
taken with a deep-focus lens, can be studied "frame by frame"
(i.e., individual pictures) and the positions of the shadows in the

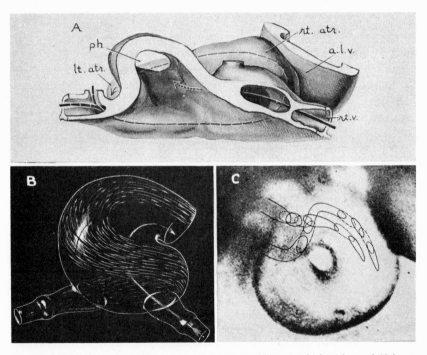

Fig. 69. Course of two blood streams through atrium of heart in chick embryo of 48 hours
incubation. (A) Caudal view of wax model of atrium; (B) dorsal view of hollow glass model
blown in the observed shape of atrium and atrioventricular canal; (C) lateral view of coiled
living heart showing successive position of blood corpuscles. Further description in text. a.l.v.
ascending limb of ventricle; lt.atr., left atrium; ph., pharynx; rt.atr., right atrium; rt.v., right
entering vein. [From originals of Figs. 1, 2, and 6, J. L. Bremer, Am. J. Anat. 49, 412, 415,
420 (1932).]

succeeding frames indicated by encircling lines of different character (Fig. 69, *C*). Because of the limitations of this method the drawing in *C* gives a right-sided view of the currents shown in *A* and *B*. Each frame represents ¹⁄₁₆ second, and the varying rapidity of the two streams is roughly indicated by the overlapping or lengthening of the areas encircled; the left stream runs fastest under the influence of the successive contractions of the right and left atrial walls. In the atrioventricular canal it appears, in the drawing, dorsal to the right stream, but actually it is also far to the left, and the two streams preserve their identities even in the narrow canal, probably because of the inherent viscosity of their plasma, which prevents any intermixture of the two bloods.[10]

For a portion of their course the two blood streams provide a guide for the growth of the ultimately continuous septum which is to divide the left and right chambers of the heart after birth. This may be the chief or even the only purpose of these two streams, for soon after the initial growth of the originally separate parts of the septum, as will be explained in the following chapter, the spiraling streams are discontinued, disorganized by a rearrangement of the entering veins. At the initiation of peristalsis both the common cardinal trunks and the two umbilical veins enter the horns of the sinus venosus from the two sides, and the sinus opens into the atrium by a broad mouth, transversely oval, a disposition that favors the formation of the two blood streams, from left and right; but after the union of the left umbilical vein with the ventral liver sinusoids to form the ductus venosus and the loss of both umbilical vein remnants in the body walls (p. 73), and after the formation of the inferior and superior venae cavae and of the azygos system (p. 89 and Fig. 48), the mouth of the sinus becomes elongated craniocaudally, and is carried to the right by the dominance of the right-sided venae cavae. The left horn of the sinus, after its component veins have made new connections, is suppressed and becomes the coronary sinus. This change in the orientation of the sinoatrial opening is sufficient to destroy the delicate mechanism of the spiral streams, and with it the peristaltic heart beat. Soon the peristalsis is replaced by the permanent heart rhythm. The originally continuous heart musculature, on which peristalsis depends, is now interrupted by a fibrous band encircling the atrioventricular region, across which only the bundle of His with its related nodes [11], [12], [13] maintains connection between atria and ventricles to initiate the normal fetal heart beat. Fortunately, the apparent purpose of the two spiral streams has been already accomplished in that the endocardial cushions and the other portions of the heart septa which parallel their course have already begun their development.

The two cavae now enter the sinus from above and below, respectively, making the sinus mouth a vertical slit, with valves to right and left. The right sinus horn is then taken into the expanding wall of the right atrium, and the two cavae and the coronary sinus now open directly into the atrium itself by three separate mouths. The left sinus valve is soon lost, but the right one remains in part as the variable valve of the inferior vena cava (of Eustachius) and that of the coronary sinus (Thebesian). In the fetus the Eustachian valve is so placed as to divert the blood from the inferior cava, including that from the placenta, toward the left atrium. The ridge formed by the upper meeting of the two original sinus valves, called the septum spurium, later spreads over the roof of the right atrium as the crista terminalis, growing to form quite a deep septum in the mid-fetal period. Before birth, however, most of this septum is destroyed by degenerative multiple fenestration and the subsequent absorption of the intervening strands. Only a low ridge on the internal surface of the atrial roof normally persists. Occasionally the unabsorbed fenestrated sheet persists as a lacelike veil, called Chiari's net, hanging from the crista terminalis into the right atrial cavity.

During these changes the tube has become marked off by constrictions and expansions into several segments. Following the course of the blood stream, the large veins from either side open into the right end of the single chambered atrium, which, however, is soon to be divided by a narrow median septum into right and left chambers; then comes a constricted segment, the *atrioventricular canal,* representing the descending limb of the cardiac loop (Fig. 70, *e, f*); next the transverse portion, making a common *ventricle,* soon to be divided into left and right ventricles by a sagittally disposed septum (*b, f*); then the ascending limb of the loop which in very young hearts (*a, b, d*) is marked by a longer or shorter constriction followed by a bulging portion, tapering to the aortic trunk. The constriction

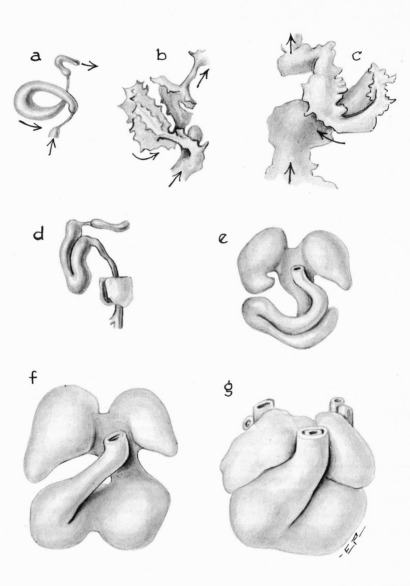

Fig. 70. Copies of drawings of models of the endothelial hearts of young human embryos up to the fifth week, gathered from the literature. Various forms of loops and development of atrial, ventricular and bulbar enlargements: (a), (b), (d), left side; (c), right side; (e), (f), (g), frontal view. [From J. L. Bremer, Arch. Path. 34, 1019 (1942).]

has been named the fretum cordis; it is normally soon reduced to a shallow external groove or is lost completely; its persistance as a broad ring-shaped internal shelf, almost separating the conus of the pulmonary trunk from the right ventricle, is called infundibular or subaortic stenosis, and noted as one of the rarest of heart anomalies.[14] These various constrictions and swellings affect primarily the endothelial heart, so that they are shown best on models of this inner layer only. It is interesting to compare the more recently made models (Fig. 70, *b, c*), with their carefully indicated tent-shaped endothelial protrusions, with the earlier models in which these supposed irregularities were smoothed over. Actually their presence is important as marking the sites of the two adult ventricles. Later the bulging of the atria is chiefly on the anterior or cranial side and hence the auricular appendages soon lie on either side of the truncus arteriosus, partly overlapping it (*g*), while the dorsal atrial wall rests on the septum transversum. When this septum, because of the caudal migration of its ventral attachment, alters its originally transverse plane to one almost vertically disposed, the heart follows the change by rotation on a transverse axis, the ventricular loop now lying caudal to the atria.

While the heart is in the coiled form the pulmonary vein makes its appearance as an endothelial outgrowth from the dorsal wall of the common atrium into the remaining portion of the dorsal mesocardium toward the developing lung bud, which springs from the ventral wall of the pharynx (Fig. 67, *I*). The venous outgrowth is in the mid-line and therefore to the left of the mouth of the sinus venosus in its final position. As the lung bud divides into right and left bronchi, the single venous outgrowth develops a branch for each lung, and these in turn produce secondary branches to upper and lower lobes. The stem and the primary branches are then taken up into the expanding wall of the atrium, and the four mouths are considered as four pulmonary veins, two for each lung. The occasional absence of one, or even two, of these veins is due to incomplete absorption of the primary branches, or to faulty branching of the primary vein. Various other anomalies of the pulmonary vein have already been described in the section on the lung (p. 43) and will be further discussed in the next chapter.

The component regions of the ascending limb of the heart loop, perhaps because they alter so rapidly with growth, have unfortunately been given various names by different writers. The wide portion distal to the fretum, called by some early anatomists the bulbus aortae, is known by others as the conus, a term referring to its later tapering distal portion. The term "bulb," as bulbus cordis, has also been applied to the right side of the transverse portion of the heart loop, corresponding to the future right ventricle, the future interventricular septum being known as bulboventricular in early embryos. By some, the whole right side of the loop is known as the bulb. There is as yet no unanimity in the use of these terms, but recent writers tend to follow the simple and expressive nomenclature, employing the terms "ventricle," "conus," and "truncus" for successive, and only in very young embryos well-defined, regions of the ascending limb of the ventricular loop. The term "bulb," however, with its compound "bulboventricular," is so well established as a synonym for right ventricle that it may well be retained as an alternate form.

9 ———

HEART, II. SEPTATION

Thus far the heart has been described as a tube with a single lumen, with no provision for the separation into venous and arterial streams, as seen in the heart after birth. Actually, in the mammalian heart in utero no such separation is necessary. The circulating blood in the young human embryo is only partially oxygenated in that the common atrium receives venous blood from the body and viscera and also arterial (better oxygenated) blood from the placenta through the umbilical vein; the blood from all sources is partially mixed in the heart before starting again on its next round. It is true that in the fetus most of the oxygenated (placental) blood passes to the left side of the heart, as in the adult, but even this is mixed with the venous blood of the two venae cavae. This condition must continue throughout fetal life, and any attempt to divide the single tube by septa will only, apparently, interfere with the passage and mixture of the blood through the heart, yet such proper septation must be ready at birth for the sudden change to air breathing, without impeding, even momentarily, the normal fetal flow.

In the last chapter it was suggested that the temporary presence of the two spiral blood streams in the early heart, while the heartbeat is purely peristaltic, might regulate the growth of certain portions of the ultimately continuous septum that finally divides the heart into its right and left channels. The individual portions occur in definite regions of the heart tube, one dividing the common atrium into right and left parts, one in the atrioventricular canal, a third between the two ventricles, and a fourth in the conus and truncus. They all are initiated by the local thickening of the endocardial tissue and its protrusion (covered of course by the endothelium) into the relatively quiet spaces between blood streams, where there may be supposed to be minimal pressure against the wall. The septum in the atrioventricular canal is the simplest and may be described first.

During the fifth week two mounds of endocardial tissue, the endocardial cushions, arise respectively on the dorsal and ventral walls of the canal (Fig. 71, *A*, *a*) and by continued growth soon meet and fuse along their flattened tops to produce a complete septum (*b*). To right and left the divided canal is reduced to narrow slits (*B*), both leading from the left side of the common atrium to the left ventricle below. In the lateral wall of each slit a smaller similar cushion arises (*B, C*). From these lateral cushions and from the opposing sides of the main endocardial mass the mitral and tricuspid valves are to be formed, as will be described later. Then the fused cushions increase in width, chiefly to the right, narrowing slightly as they do so, in that the cranial surface of the fused endo-

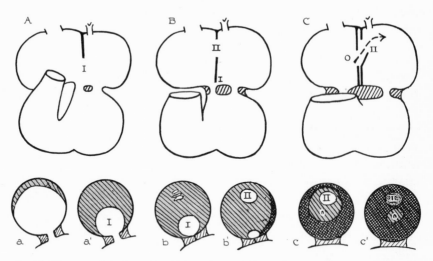

Fig. 71. Diagrams of the formation of the atrioventricular and interatrial septa. (*Upper row*) Frontal sections of heart at different stages: (A) endocardial cushions (diagonal lines) enlarging successively toward the right (left of page); atrial septum primum with foramen I; (B) septum primum with foramena I and II; (C) septum primum with foramen II, and septum secundum with foramen ovale O. (*Lower row*) Right lateral view of interatrial passage. The endocardial cushions are seen fusing; the two interatrial septa are shown by different shading and marking. Description in text.

cardial mass slants a little caudally (*C*), causing the future tricuspid valve to lie at a noticeably lower level than the mitral valve. The dextral expansion continues until the right canal becomes a direct connection between the right atrium and the right ventricle (*C*), a connection that entails the reduction of the deep cleft between the two ventricular limbs of the cardiac loop (Fig. 70, *f*). This is accomplished by the fusion of the opposing walls of the conus and left ventricle (Fig. 70, *g*), making an internal conoventricular (or bulboventricular) ridge, which is then promptly absorbed. After this absorption, the right atrioventricular passage opens directly into the right ventricle. If this fusion and ridge formation extend too far cranially, above the fused endocardial cushions (as may happen if the heart is unusually tightly coiled), and include the ventral wall of the right atrium and the dorsal wall of the cranial section of the conus, just below the valves, the wall between these two cavities will remain membranous; if subsequent absorption of this wall occurs, an open passage will exist from the lower right atrium, above the tricuspid valve, to the upper conus. Since this portion of the conus is later to become the vestibule of the left ventricle, this anomalous connection between the two sides of the heart is called an atriovestibular foramen or fistula.

The interatrial septum,[1] destined to divide the common atrial cavity into two separate chambers, comprises two members. The first starts as a narrow, linear sagittal thickening of the endocardium on the dorsocaudal wall of the atrium (Fig. 71, *A, a*) to the left of the entering veins. This region is also a quiet one, for the left spiral venous stream at this point follows the cranial wall of the atrium. With growth the septum becomes a deep, sagittally directed crescent (*a, a'*), the two horns extending cranially and caudally around the atrial wall toward the two endocardial cushions, and in this course the cranial wing of the crescent seems destined to cut across the left spiral blood stream as it runs from right to left along the common atrial roof (Fig. 71, *B*). By the time this crescent wing has advanced thus far, however, the early peristaltic type of heartbeat has been superseded by the adult type, with more uniform current. Only in one rare type of anomaly, in which the interatrial septum is swept to the left atrial wall (Fig. 72, *G*) is the force of the roof stream indicated, and this condition is probably due to the precocious growth of the septum while the spiral blood streams still flowed. Normally, with altered heartbeat, the septum can cross the interatrial passage without hindrance, and seems destined to separate completely the right and left atrial chambers.

Complete separation, in the embryo and fetus, of the right and left halves of the common atrium by continued growth of this first septum must, however, be avoided for two reasons. In the first place the blood from the placenta, the only source of oxygen and food, enters the right atrium and, to supply the fetal body through the aorta, must cross to the left side; and, secondly, since before birth the pulmonary circulation is minimal, a sufficient flow through the left heart is necessary to insure its proper growth, for blood vessels enlarge and develop their muscular coats only in response to the increase in blood flow. For both these reasons the interatrial passage must be kept partially open, yet after birth the passage must be soon closed to prevent the mixture of oxygenated and unoxygenated blood. To meet these conditions the interatrial septum, in human embryos, is formed by the union and partial fusion of two individual, closely parallel ingrowths from the wall of the common atrial cavity, called septum primum (septum I) and septum secundum (septum II), respectively, from the order of their appearance.

With the continued growth of septum I the two horns of the crescent reach, respectively, the dextral ends of the dorsal and ventral endocardial cushions. The space enclosed by the horns diminishes with the further broadening of the crescent-shaped septum (Fig. 71, *a*, *b*), but long before it is ultimately obliterated the septum itself, at a point near its first appearance and at a short distance from the atrial wall, develops a number of small slitlike perforations which soon fuse to form a single large defect (Fig. 71, *b*, *c*). The effect is as though the septum, stretched to its limit, had ripped at its weakest spot, but the uniformity with which this second foramen develops, in time and position, bespeaks a different, though unknown, explanation. Septum I is thus never complete: its two perforations are known as ostium I and II of septum I.

Meanwhile a second similar septum develops, septum II, just to the right of the first, but starting from the cranioventral wall of the atrium and with the horns of its crescent pointing toward the entrance of the sinus venosus (Fig. 71, *b', c*). In this case, the crescent is slender, and grows completely around the atrial wall, leaving an eccentrically placed central foramen in an otherwise complete septum. The opening is the foramen ovale (*c, c'*); its thickened rim is known as the limbus. It lies normally opposite that band of septum I which remains between its two ostia, I and II, and the two septa are so close together that the persisting band of septum I acts as a valvelike covering for the foramen ovale. By lifting this valve, blood can flow from right to left through the foramen ovale of septum II and ostium II of septum I (Fig. 71, *C*), but return is prevented by the pressure of septum I against the limbus. This condition, present during the seventh week, persists until after birth when, with the increased pressure in the left atrium caused by the greater flow from the pulmonary veins, the valve gradually—not suddenly—closes by fusion with the limbus. The foramen ovale becomes the shallow fossa ovalis, and the two septa fuse throughout. In a large percentage of cases, however, the fusion remains permanently incomplete to the extent that a probe can readily be passed beneath the edge of the limbus toward and through ostium II of septum I, showing that the passage between atria is anatomically open, though functionally closed.

What the meaning may be of this complicated use of two septa and three ostia is not understood. It has been pointed out that the continuous perforation of the interatrial septum during fetal life, with some type of valve action to prevent return flow, is necessary for the proper growth of the left side of the heart, yet in the chick a single septum suffices, with multiple perforations in place of ostium II, controlled by muscle fibers within the intervening strands capable of closing the foramina by their contraction during systole. The presence of two septa is a mammalian characteristic, but even among mammals there are variations in the mode of formation of the second septum. In the pig it begins as a continuation of the lower end of the left sinus valve and sweeps backward over the roof of the atrium in a crescent; in man the crescent is normally unrelated to the diminishing sinus valves. In certain mammals foramen II is at first represented by fenestration of the entire septum, as in birds, and yet is reinforced by a second septum. Whatever the advantage in this double protection, a distinct disadvantage is evident in the many types of anomaly to which the two septa are liable.

Of the anomalies of the interatrial septa[2] by far the most common is the open or unguarded foramen ovale after birth. This condition is due to the malposition or excessive size of foramen II or of the foramen ovale, or of both, so that the two openings overlap. In certain cases the central portion or all of septum I is pierced by a group of fenestrations, to such an extent that the valvula foraminis ovalis, that part of septum I forming the floor of the fossa ovalis, is represented by strands with wide spaces between. Less frequently, the lower end of septum I appears incomplete, as though through the persistence of foramen I of septum I. This cannot be the actual cause for this anomaly, however, for the growth of septum II would effectively close such a gap. Actually, the same effect can be obtained if the flat tops of the two endocardial cushions fail to meet—a condition known as persistent common atrioventricular canal[3]—or meet only on a portion of their surfaces, leaving a cleft soon bridged over by septum II in its growth around the wall of the common atrium. The abnormality is in the endocardial cushions (and probably accompanied by a further malformation of the mitral and tricuspid valves derived from them), rather than in the atrial septa. Through the resulting connection between the atria, the arterial and venous blood may readily mix to cause one type of "blue baby," yet this anomaly is occasionally compatible with normal life, having been found accidentally in active individuals of middle age. Complete absence of both atrial septa is found in cor biventriculum triloculare or cor biloculare.[4]

Another type of anomaly depends on the malposition of the interatrial septa. Septum II may develop too far to the right (Fig. 72, *A*), leaving a larger or smaller triangular space between the two. A variation of this type is the entrance of one or more pulmonary veins into this middle space (Fig. 72, *B*), while the use of the right cusp of the valve of the sinus venosus as the basis of septum II brings the systemic blood into this anomalous central atrial chamber (Fig. 72, *C*). In these cases the foramina in the two septa permit a nearly normal flow of blood during intrauterine life, but since the foramina thus separated in the two septa must remain unclosed after birth the mixture of bloods postnatally is inevitable.

An entirely different pattern of atrial septation is caused by the premature development of fibromuscular tissue in the form of a resistant band encircling some part of the thin atrial wall, which in the subsequent expansion of the heart draws a fold of atrial wall across the lumen as an incomplete septum. In some cases[5] the fibrous band encircles the mouth of the originally single pulmonary venous trunk, and the subsequent expansion of this trunk, which normally is included in the atrial wall, now forms a rounded sinus, receiving the four pulmonary veins and opening through the hole in the septum to the remainder of the left atrium below (Fig. 72, D, E). In another case an almost complete septum divided the left atrium into dorsal and ventral compartments, the former having on its mesial wall the foramen ovale, the latter opening through the mitral valve (Fig. 72, F). Here also the causative factor is probably an early fibrous band, for no portion of the interatrial septa could

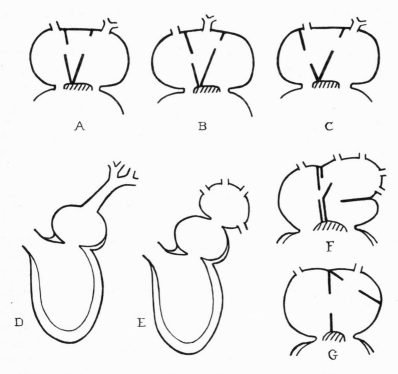

Fig. 72. Various anomalous positions of the interatrial septa. Described in text.

assume this position. As variations of this type the abnormal atrial septum may be without opening, the pulmonary blood passing by the bronchial veins to the right atrium, and thus to the lower compartment of the left atrium through the foramen ovale; or the new septum may be in part represented by fibromuscular cords,[6] similar to the chordae tendineae of the atrioventricular valves.

The interventricular septum begins as a narrow internal ridge continuing caudally from the center of the dorsal endocardial cushion, after the latter has so far expanded to the right that the right atrioventricular passage opens into the right ventricle (Fig. 71, *C*). The low ridge lengthens sagitally, at first between the two heart streams, and then partially encircles the transverse portion of the common ventricle (the bottom of the original heart loop) to appear again on its ventral wall. During this course it tends to block the caudal transverse portion of the current from the left ventricle and to deflect it cranially. On either side of this low septum the two future ventricles are formed. Although in the adult heart the ventricles appear side by side and contract simultaneously as though paired expansions, embryologically they are placed tandem-wise along the primitive heart tube and, as long as the driving force is peristaltic, the left ventricle beats before the right. They are at first recognizeable as rounded bulges on the outer side of the ring-shaped heart, with the shallow interventricular groove between them, matched within the lumen by the low interventricular septum, marking the same-named canal.

In these bulging pockets the epimyocardium, during the early part of the sixth week, becomes divided into a thin inner and a thicker outer coat with loose mesenchymal tissue between them, the inner coat consisting of circularly disposed premuscular strands closely wrapped around the endothelium, like a cord wound around a rubber tube. Where the two curves are sharpest the strands of this inner layer separate slightly on the outer side of the curve, and through the gaps thus formed the endothelium sends sprouts which follow the delicate subendothelial fibrils present in the mesenchyma and spread and anastomose as sinusoids in the loose tissue between the two muscle layers (Fig. 73). Soon muscular strands from the inner layer follow between the sinusoids, growing peripherally as the trabeculae carneae to join the cortical muscles. The interventricular septum increases in height both by its own growth and by the expansion of the two ventricles on either side of it, until it becomes a sagittaly disposed, crescent-shaped curtain attached to the inner surface of the interventricular wall, with its dorsal horn resting on the dorsal atrioventricular cushion, near the right end, its ventral horn following the ventral wall of the interventricular passage. It partially surrounds this passage, and plays an important part in its final closure, as will be explained later.

At the atrial ends of the ventricles this same penetration by sinusoids produces the mitral and tricuspid valves. It will be remembered that the originally single atrioventricular canal is divided by the fusion of the two endocardial cushions, and that two minor lateral cushions face the ends of the main pair. The advancing sinusoids soon attack all of these cushions from the ventricular

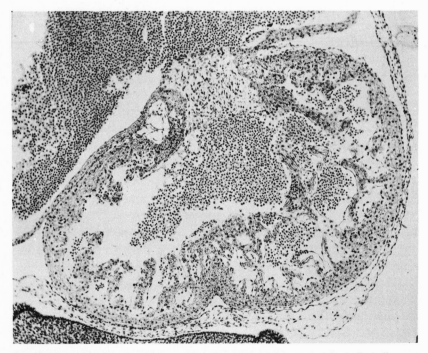

Fig. 73. Photograph of a transverse section through the lower part of the bulb, bulboventricular canal, and left ventricle of a human embryo of 5 weeks, 6.7 mm, to show the early growth of sinusoids between the separated strands of the inner muscle layer. The curved row of cross-cut muscle strands at the tops of the trabeculae carneae in the right ventricle indicate the former size of the tubular heart. [From J. L. Bremer, Arch. Path. 34, 1016 (1942).]

side, replacing most of the looser mesenchyma, but leaving the denser upper surface layers, which are to become the valves proper, and the denser mesenchymal strands, which are to form the chordae tendineae that attach the valves to the fibrous ring of the heart or to the ventricular musculature. For the mitral valves the lateral cushion and the left half of the median cushion suffice to form the two leaflets; in the triscupid valve the third cusp is variously described as arising from a special tubercle at the right end of the ventral cushion or from the lower end of the septum dividing the cardiac conus,[7] soon to be described.

In certain anomalous cases one or more of the cusps of the mitral or tricuspid valves may be ineffective because of the abnormal shortness of its chordae tendineae and the malformation of the papillary muscles; the leaflets are short, fused, thickened, and often semicartilaginous. The valve then leaks since the cusps are unable to meet on closing. This condition may well be caused by the imperfect activity of the burrowing sinusoids, their failure to excavate a sufficient quantity of the subendothelial tissue encircling the atrioventricular canals. In other cases the cushions may be so insufficiently undercut that the leaflets remain thick and stiff, causing a condition of stenosis. Surgical treatment of the isolated form of mitral stenosis—mitral valvulotomy—is now a recognized procedure.[8, 9]

The fourth group of heart partitions develops in the conus and truncus as a pair of narrow, opposing endocardial cushions or ridges, running lengthwise of the heart tube and following in their course its inherent dextral spiral torsion, thereby showing that they have already begun their growth while the two guiding blood streams are still present, before the growth of the interatrial septa have interfered with their flow. The course of the two streams [10] in this distal part of the heart can be traced in the drawing of two originally parallel rubber tubes (Fig. 74, A), representing the two streams, forced into the known spiral form in the atrial region and separated widely just below to indicate the spread to the right of the endocardial cushions. These regions are readily identified in the cast model (B) of the heart of a chick embryo of about 6 days; the atria bulge widely at the sharper curves of the original venous stream from the left side of the body, the interatrial septum (single in the bird) shows as a deep sagittal cleft in the wax, and the two atrioventricular passages appear as slender vertical strips of wax, separated by the wide space representing the fused endocardial cushions. The two sets of ventricular sinusoids (here cut short) sprout from the two streams as they turn sharply upward, the interventricular septum between them.

The more distal part of the heart streams, in conus and truncus, follow closely the pattern of the two parallel rubber tubes. Between the two blood streams, here as in the atrioventricular canal, two endocardial cushions arise from the opposite walls of the single heart tube, and by their subsequent fusion divide it into two daughter tubes. In the conus and truncus the cushions take the form of elongated ridges, paralleling the streams and following their spiral trend. According to most writers these ridges are not at first continuous, but originate in three separate regions, each pair then growing caudally, against the blood stream, to meet the one below; others[11] recognize two preliminary continuous low ridges with more rapid growth at three points. At these points are produced respectively the septum aorticopulmonale, the truncus ridges, and the conus ridges, the two latter pairs being often designated as the distal

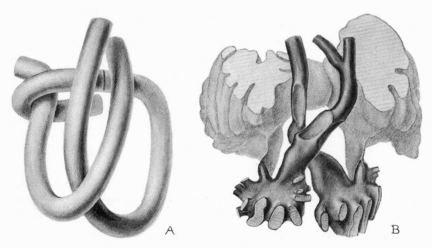

Fig. 74. (A) Paired rubber tubes coiled to represent the courses of the two heart streams. (B) Model of the cavities of the heart of a chick embryo of 5 days incubation (Boyden); the sinusoids are represented as cut away near the main heart lumen. [From originals of Figs. 7 and 9, J. L. Bremer, Am. J. Anat. 42, 363, 364 (1928).]

and proximal bulbar ridges. The septum aorticopulmonale continues caudally the notch between the paired fourth and pulmonary arches as they branch from the primitive aortic trunk; the truncus and conus ridges start at the distal ends of these two regions. From these three points the respective ridges grow caudally.

Where the truncus and conus meet, the two ridges become abruptly much broader and higher for a short distance, and between them two new intercalated endocardial cushions arise from the conal wall. These four moundlike endocardial thickenings are to form the semilunar valves, in the same way that the paired primary endocardial cushions of the atrioventricular canal, together with the lesser pair on its lateral walls, are used to form the mitral and tricuspid valves. Most writers, with a few dissenters, place these abrupt thickenings in the territory of the conus instead of in that of the truncus, at the beginning of a region of growth instead of at its end, and this theory is strengthened by the occasional finding of an open connection between aorta and pulmonary trunk (aortic septal defect) just above the valves, indicating the absence or non-union of ridges locally at that point, which can best be explained as a persistent gap between two successive sets of ridges. If such an anastomosis is tubular, and not a side-to-side union, its surgical closure may now be successfully accomplished.[12] A similar, but rarer, side-to-side anastomosis of aorta and pulmonary trunk an inch or more above the valves may indicate the discontinuity of the septum aorticopulmonare and the truncus ridges.

The semilunar valves and the coronary vessels. When the broad conal ridges fuse to divide the single conus into aortic and pulmonary streams, three ridges appear in each daughter tube—one minor (intercalated) ridge and one half of each major ridge (Fig. 75, *a, b*). The aortic and pulmonary semilunar valves are shaped from the abrupt proximal ends of the four ridges, undercut to form the sinuses of Valsalva. After the complete separation of the two trunks has extended to just below the level of the valves, new growth forces slightly rotate each vessel so that the matching cusps are no longer in line in the adult (*d*). Moreover, the valves are not at the same level and do not lie in quite the same plane, for as the embryonic truncus curves dorsally to leave the pericardial cavity, its ventral (pulmonary) half, and therefore the pulmonary valve, lies at a slightly more cranial level; the dorsal half, and hence the plane of the aortic valve, is tilted dorsally.

In addition to stenosis or stresia, which indicate overgrowth or faulty excavation of the mounds of tissue that form the cranial ends of the conal ridges, the anomalies of the semilunar valves, more often aortic than pulmonary, are confined to the increase or decrease of the number of cusps, the former caused by the splitting of one of the normal components, the latter probably by the agenesis of an intercalated ridge.

The coronary arteries in the rabbit[13] and pig, and presumably also in man, arise in response to the need of the constantly increasing cardiac musculature, which, as it forms a thicker layer in the ventricles and extends cranially onto the conus, can no longer be adequately supplied through the sinusoids from the heart lumen. Since the conus on its dorsal side is partially supported by the ventral atrial wall, the muscular extension is more advanced on its

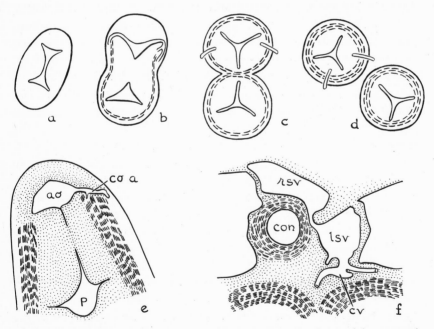

Fig. 75. (a–d) Diagrams to show the formation of the semilunar valves and the outgrowth of the coronary arteries; described in text. Drawings of (e) left coronary artery and (f) coronary vein in pig embryo of 12.0 mm. ao, aorta; co a, coronary artery; con, conus; cv, coronary vein; lsv, rsv, left and right horns of sinus venosus; p, pulmonary trunk.

ventral and lateral walls; and in the region of the valves, during the seventh week of embryonic life, the dorsal intercalated cushion is the only one not resting on a muscular base. Taking advantage of this local absence of supporting muscle, two arterial sprouts bud out from the aortic endothelium at the bottom of the two grooves between the dorsal cushion and the opposing right and left conal ridges (Fig. 75, *b, e*). From this position the new vessels can reach the pericardium, skirting the advancing edge of the muscle sheet, and proceed as coronary arteries, giving off many branches to the underlying muscles and connecting infrequently with the sinusoids from the heart lumen.[14] Later changes in relative position and the continued thickening of the ventricular walls draw the coronary trunks to a more ventral course, and in response the coronary mouths gradually migrate around the aortic wall until they open within the left and the anterior sinuses of Valsalva, respectively.

The coronary arteries may be either increased or decreased in number, or may arise from an abnormal source. An additional vascular sprout on either side, from the proper groove, but above or below the normal artery, is not uncommon. On the other hand, if the groove on either side of the aortic intercalated mound is covered at an early date by the precociously advancing conal musculature, no sprout will appear. The single remaining coronary artery usually branches to supply both sides of the heart, but very rarely the territory normally supplied by the missing artery is taken over by an extension from the systemic arteries accompanying the aorta from above. In transposition of the great vessels (p. 158) the pulmonary trunk may, by detorsion, be brought nearly into the normal position of the aorta, and there, lacking any musculature, produce a left or right coronary artery. Of all these coronary anomalies, this last only is of serious clinical importance, since it necessarily leads to damage to the appropriate ventricular wall, through lack of oxygen after birth.

The veins of the heart are derived simply by outgrowth from the left horn of the sinus venosus, later called the coronary sinus (Fig. 75, *f*). They may connect with the ventricular sinusoids, but no definite circulation is established through these channels, and even in cases of coronary occlusion (of one artery) they are not called into play. After such occlusion, relief most often follows by the anastomosia between small branches of the two coronary arteries; recently surgical relief has been offered by the implantation of a branch of the internal mammary artery directly into the ventricular musculature,[15] or by the suturing of a portion of mesentery (brought through the diaphragm for this purpose) to the scarified surface of the ventricle,[16] thus establishing an extraneous cardiac circulation.

The major conus ridges continue their dextral spiral course and the plane of the future septum caused by their fusion is correspondingly spiral. The ridge that is in the left position at the level of the valves meets and fuses with the ventral horn of the interventricular septum. The two minor ridges fade out after having produced their respective valve cusps; and the right ridge (right at the level of the valves) runs to the dorsal side of the conus and there meets the upper end of the right atrioventricular canal, where it divides into two branches, one following the ventral surface of each wall of the slit. The mesial branch follows the dorsal wall of the atriovestibular foramen, where it may form, in part, the anterior portion of the mesial cusp of the tricuspid valve. The lateral branch may similarly take part in the formation of the anterior cusp. A third branch of the ridge, coming off at a higher level (or a recrudescence of the ventral intercalated ridge), sweeps over the top of the right ventricle to the right dorsal wall as the crista supraventricularis. This fanning out of the right conus ridge into three widely spaced branches might be expected as the result of the expansion of the relatively narrow conus into the much larger ventricle. Between the free lower border of the septum joining the major conus ridges and the edge of the interventricular septum lies the interventricular or bulboventricular foramen.

The final step in the separation of the aortic and pulmonary streams follows during the ninth week by the closure of the two fetal foramina already mentioned. The atriovestibular foramen is closed by the delayed growth of the right end of the ventral endocardial cushion in the form of a thin membrane. The interventricular foramen is closed by continued growth of the conal septum, of the eudocardial cushions, and of the free edge of the interventricular septum, each supplying a share.[17] According to some authors, the component from the anterior cushion supplies by far the greatest share.[18] The two closures together form the septum membranaceum, part of which is above the valve. Both are subject to arrest of development, the lower more frequently because of its tripartite origin, giving the common anomaly called defect at the base, or patent interventricular foramen.

As an anomaly, the septum in the conus and truncus is said by some writers to be occasionally eccentrically placed, with variation in size of the two resulting vessels and in the number of valve cusps,[19] but the fact that similar differences in size may also occur as the result of any malformations entailing differences in the amount of blood passing through the vessels suggests a better reasoning. Complete absence of the septum is found in persistent conus arteriosus (truncus communis), yet even in this condition there cannot have been a total agenesis of the paired ridges, for the accompanying single valve, usually of four cusps, is in the position of the normal semilunar valves and indicates the former presence of the enlarged distal ends of the truncus ridges and of the two extra intercalated cushions from which the four cusps are formed. The common vessel drains both ventricles and supplies, beside the usual systemic branches, both coronary and pulmonary arteries, the latter occasionally using the open ductus arteriosus as a common trunk.

Combined malformations of the heart.[20] Any one of the various septa that normally divide the heart may singly fail to complete its mission, and any one of the valves formed in connection with the septa may be imperfect. Agenesis of individual septa may lead to various forms of cor biloculare or triloculare, or truncus communis. Lesser failures result in interatrial or interventricular defects, or anomalies of the atrioventricular or semilunar valves. Such individual abnormalities are rarely encountered, however, for the very fact of their early presence so alters the flow of blood that other valves or septa along the course of the same stream distally are secondarily affected and by this fact may mask the original abnormalities. For instance, an early stenosis of the mitral valve may result in an abnormally small left ventricle with thin wall and stenosed aortic valve and aorta, for with reduced inflow the distal portions of the heart will not grow to their normal proportions. On the other hand, the mitral stenosis may, by the same reasoning, be secondary to the precocious narrowing of the interatrial foramina. Such sequences would be definitely predictable were it not for the incomplete interventricular and interatrial septa of early fetal life, through either of which openings the blood volume of the two sides could be equalized, thus allowing the distal structures in the sequence to undergo normal development.

Isolated malformations of the septa and valves do appear, nevertheless. The variations in position occasionally displayed by the two original interatrial septa and their varying relations to the entering veins have already been described (p. 146). Persistent open foramen ovale or interventricular septal defects, and variations in the number and form of the cusps of the various valves may, if they do not interfere seriously with the proper flow of the blood streams, persist as individual anomalies. So also may the variations of the coronary arteries. Stenosis of the pulmonary valve, if it is of developmental origin, is always accompanied by septal defects and other changes in the heart; if of late origin it remains individual and unaccompanied by either septal or valvular alterations.[21] The difference in effect is due to the fact that the late narrowing is always of inflammatory origin, due to valvular endocarditis occurring in late fetal life, which may proceed to atresia of the valve. This type of pulmonary-valve stenosis is, then, strictly not an anomaly, but an incident in the course of a fetal disease. Many writers fail to recognize the fundamental difference between the two conditions, and tend to consider all abnormalities of the valves as due to fetal disease. Shaner,[22] however, who has studied the hearts of many thousands of pig embryos, finds the endocardial tissue invariably quite normal during the weeks when true embryonic anomalies are formed; this suggests that only those individual anomalies without accompanying changes in the distal heart are caused by disease,[23] but does not preclude the disease of an already abnormal valve.

10 ———

HEART, III. TRANSPOSITION OF
THE GREAT VESSELS

In addition to the several anomalous variations in the position or effectiveness of the septa and valves of the heart, another group of anomalies concerns a change in the relative position of the aortic and pulmonary trunks. The normal spiral course of these vessels as they ascend from the left and right ventricles, respectively, is so striking that any marked change in this pattern is obvious at a glance. The picture is one of the unwinding or detorsion of the normal heart spiral. Lesser grades of this malformation are not so readily recognized; the least of these, in which the base of the aorta has moved only slightly to the right, but enough to be in position to drain both ventricles in the absence of the membranous interventricular septum, is called overriding or dextroposition of the aorta, and all gradations between this and the complete exchange of position between the two vessels, with the aorta arising from the right ventricle and the pulmonary trunk apparently from the left, are possible and have been designated as numbered types[1] (Fig. 76).

The condition is always accompanied by related abnormalities within the heart itself. Failure of the membranous interventricular septum is constant, for this structure depends on the correct alignment of the conal septum with the endocardial cushions and the muscular interventricular septum, and the plane of the conal septum is necessarily altered by the detorsion of the trunks. Other changes include the displacement and enlargement of the crista supraventricularis, the variation in size of the ventricles and the

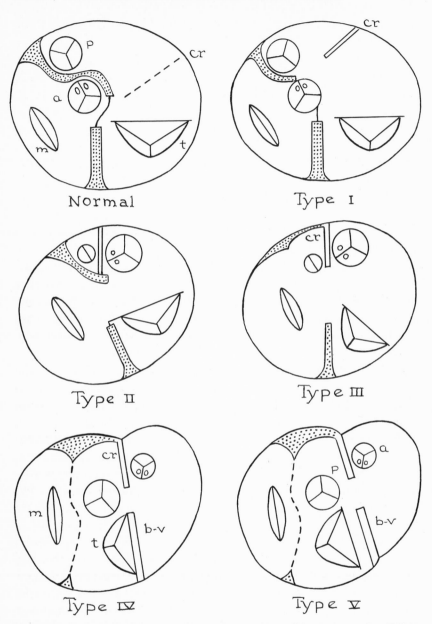

Fig. 76. Diagrams to show the various types of transposition of the great vessels. (Slightly altered from Harris and Farber.) *a*, aorta, showing openings of coronary arteries; *p*, pulmonary artery; *m*, *t*, mitral and tricuspid valves; *cr*, crista supraventricularis; *b–v*, bulboventricular ridge; interventricular septum is stippled.

thickness of their walls, variation in size of the vessels themselves, and patent foramen ovale or ductus arteriosus. Two of the more common combinations of such changes are known by the names of those who have best described them. The tetralogy of Fallot comprises a large overriding aorta, interventricular septal defect, hypertrophy of the right ventricular wall and of the crista supra-ventricularis, and pulmonary stenosis. In extreme cases the pulmonary trunk may be reduced to a fibrous cord. The less common Eisenmenger's complex combines dextroposition of the aorta, inter-ventricular septal defect, a large right ventricle, and normal or en-larged pulmonary trunk and valves. In the first case the aorta receives a portion of the blood from the right ventricle, which there-fore develops an increased musculature to drive this extra quotient through the sytemic vessels, while the reduced pulmonary flow in-duces pulmonary stenosis. In the second case the aorta is not quite so far to the right, and thus drains only its normal ventricle, while the septal defect permits the flow of blood to the right, with conse-quent enlargement of the right ventricle and often of the pulmonary trunk and valve. In this latter instance the size of the interven-tricular septal defect seems to be the deciding factor. These two conditions constitute Type I.

In any case of stenosis of the pulmonary trunk the lungs are in danger of receiving too little blood for the proper oxygenation of the body after birth. In this condition two makeshift mechanisms may be brought into play. First, the ductus arteriosus may remain open post partum and transmit blood to the lungs from the aorta by a reversal of the normal course of the blood flow. It is probably this connection in fetal life that ensures the normal growth and expansion of the fetal lungs in cases of congenital pulmonary stenoses. Second, if the ductus closes in the usual manner after birth, the bronchial arteries may enlarge and send to the lungs the normal fetal quota of blood, which, by the simultaneous enlargement of the normal capillary connections between the bronchial and pul-monary circulations (p. 42), is returned to the heart chiefly by way of the pulmonary veins. Both mechanisms are inefficient in that the lungs receive in part already oxygenated blood. Life is maintained only by the mixture of bloods through an interatrial or interventricular defect.

Type II is known as simple transposition. It is characterized by a further migration of the aorta, which now arises directly from the right ventricle close to the pulmonary trunk, from which it is separated by the hypertrophied and displaced crista supraventricularis. The interventricular defect is very wide. The pulmonary trunk is stenotic, for it arises from the small compartment of the right ventricle between the anterior interventricular septum and the deep crista, which in great measure cuts it off from the rest of the ventricle. Conversely, the aorta is increased in diameter since it must transmit most of the blood from both ventricles.

Type III is called *crossed transposition* and is by far the most common of these anomalies. It also most clearly deserves the name of transposition of the great vessels for the aorta arises from the right ventricle and the pulmonary trunk (apparently) from the left, in reverse of the normal relations. The aortic orifice lies somewhat ventral to the pulmonary orifice, and the two trunks run parallel to each other, without the normal spiral twist. The pulmonary trunk may or may not be stenosed.

Type III differs from the much rarer Type II chiefly in the complete absence of the ventral interventricular septum and the increased hypertrophy of the crista supraventricularis, which now forms a new ventral septum in place of the lost one. Functionally, the pulmonary trunk arises from the left ventricle, as described, but developmentally it is still in the same small compartment of the bulbar ventricle as in Type II. The true ventral septum is often demonstrable in the form of a low ridge on the left ventral heart wall to mark the actual boundary between the two ventricles. It has already been shown (p. 148) that the interventricular septum originally consists of such a low ridge corresponding to the shallow bulboventricular groove externally, and is built up to its normal height chiefly by the individual expansion of the two ventricles due to the burrowing of the sinusoids in each, the solid wall between the two groups of sinusoids forming the core of the augmented septum; in the absence of sinusoids on one or both sides the ridge remains low. The pulmonary trunk may retain the stenosis acquired in Type II, or it may expand with its now increased volume of blood from the whole left ventricle.

Type IV, called mixed transposition, is essentially the same as crossed transposition (Type III), but with the added complication that both atria open through their customary valves into the left ventricle. The term "mixed" refers to the fact that both arterial and venous valves are deranged. In the diagram this disposition of the valves is portrayed as due to the production of a new posterior septum to the right of the tricuspid valve. This new dorsal septum is often considered to be the intensified tricuspid ledge, to which the base of the anterior cusp of the tricuspid valve is attached, re-oriented for a new purpose; but this identification is scarcely tenable, for, as has already been shown, the base of the anterior leaflet of the tricuspid valve is derived from the middle branch of the dorsal conal ridge (p. 152), and in transposition this ridge, still retaining its former relation to the two great vessels, has been rotated to the anterior wall of the ventricle. To understand the abnormal opening of the tricuspid valve into the left ventricle it is only necessary to recall the early changes in the atrioventricular canal. The canal primarily connects the common atrium with the left ventricle (Fig. 71, *A*), but as the endocardial cushions fuse and expand, the right channel is forced to the right (*B*) until it enters the upper end of the bulbar limb (*C*), a connection made possible by the obliteration of the bulboventricular or conoventricular groove. An arrest of this migration before the last step in the sequence would result in the condition seen in Type IV. The dorsal septum between the tricuspid valve and the conus is the inner ridge corresponding to the outer bulboventricular groove, still present. An arrest of development at a little earlier date shows a narrow strip of the top of the left ventricle between the tricuspid valve and the internal bulboventricular ridge (Type V). In both these types the tricuspid valve is apt to be malformed, since two of its cusps depend for their completion on the presence of the branches of one of the conus ridges. The condition of mixed transposition is thus due to two separate and unrelated abnormalities acting simultaneously on different parts of the same heart.

Life with crossed transposition of the great vessels, of any of the types so far mentioned, is sustained only by a mixture of venous and arterial blood. The condition is often designated as *"uncorrected."* Yet under certain circumstances *"corrected transposition"* is possible, with venous blood going to the lung and arterial blood to the body.

The correction is caused by an equal transposition of the veins. In describing the origin of the inferior vena cava (p. 89) it is pointed out that the fusion of the right dorsal lobe of the liver with the dorsal body wall offers the vein a direct pathway to the right horn of the sinus venosus, later part of the right atrium. The pulmonary veins always arise near the median line to meet the lung buds, and so normally to the left of the vena cava. In situs inversus of most of the viscera, including the liver, but leaving the heart still in situs solitus, the venae cavae lie to the left and enter the left atrium, and the pulmonary veins open into that on the right. Transposition of the great vessels under these circumstances result in the entrance of oxygenated blood into the right ventricle and its transmission through the transposed aorta to the body, while the venae cavae, by left atrium and left ventricle, connect with the transposed pulmonary trunk and the lungs. The same result is attained by situs solitus of the viscera in conjunction with situs inversus of the transposed heart. Both combinations are obviously very rare.

Most writers see in the unusual transposed position of the great vessels evidence of the detorsion of the bulbar region of the heart, an unwinding of the dextral spiral commonly recognized as a part of the normal development of this organ. The cause of this unwinding has been the subject of several theories. One theory[2] postulates that the heart tube is rotated around its axis in two sections, each with its own countertorsion, one in the region of the atrial canal and one in the region of the semilunar valves; that the two are independent of each other, and that in transposition the semilunar torsion fails to take place. Others [3, 4, 5] suggest that the dextral rotation in the upper part of the tube has been completed normally, but that a sinistral torsion has developed in the lower part so that the two opposites cancel each other and parallel vessels result. A completely different approach to the problem is offered in Spitzer's theory,[1] which suggests that the anomalous position of the vessels represents an atavistic reversion to the reptilian condition, in which two aortic trunks are normally present, one arising from the left ventricle, one from the right: from the right ventricle the pulmonary trunk also arises, but in a more ventral position, and between the pulmonary and the right aortic vessels runs a ridge that has been identified as the crista supraventricularis. The lost right aorta is represented in man by a more or less prominent niche in the wall between the crista and the base of the anterior cusp of the tricuspid valve. By this theory the overriding of the aorta can be explained as the reappearance of the right aorta in close relation with the left trunk, which is thus drawn to meet and fuse with it. In the other types of transposition the right aorta alone persists, arising from the right ventricle as in reptiles. The left aorta, unlike that in reptiles, is at the same time obliterated. Even in this theory the increasing degrees of transposition shown in the various types indicate a certain amount of detorsion or sinsitral rotation. In none of these theories is there any attempt to explain why the supposed changes occur and in none have known facts of embryology been critically considered.

From the embryological point of view the various types of transposition indicate increasing degrees of detorsion of the normal dextral spiral in the ascending limb of the heart loop, that part which becomes the bulbus, conus, and truncus in the embryo, later the right ventricle and the aortic and pulmonary trunks. The adult aorta is a part of this limb, separated from the pulmonary trunk by the spiral ridges within, and finally transferred to the left ventricle, or more correctly to the interventricular canal, by the late growth of the interventricular septum, of composite origin. It also must be affected by any failure of rotation or any actual detorsion that may occur. The inner ridges are an inherent part of the tube and their spiral course is inherent in the spiral torsion of the tube as a whole. Any suggestion that their course may be reversed within the still normally rotated tube must be looked at askance. So the problem of transposition may be reduced to the search for some cause or causes for the failure or partial failure of the normal dextral rotation of the truncus and conus, or for the reduction of that rotation after it has been established.

The primary cause for the dextral spiral within the heart tube is the ring form of the heart, acquired as a means of accommodating greater length within a confined space. In the group of young human hearts already shown, one (Fig. 70, d) stands out as unusual in not showing this normal ring form. The atrioventricular canal is long, the ventricular limb is correspondingly shortened and is folded back so as to point caudally, and at the level of the caudal limit of the atria the tube is again folded sharply on itself, until the conus points forward and lies parallel to the ventricle. The whole figure has the appearance of a much crushed and flattened *S*. It is of interest that the hearts of some fishes are of nearly this form. If there is no deviation of the bulb to the right and the whole heart lies in one sagittal plane, no ring will form and no dextral torsion will occur in the conus and truncus; if with continued growth of this heart the ventricular limb does slip by to the right, approaching the ring form, more and more torsion will appear.

In theory this form of heart might result in crossed transposition. The now transverse bulboventricular ridge might be absorbed, as in normal development, throwing the ventricular and bulbar limbs into one large ventricle, entered from behind by both tricuspid and mitral passages. The septum within the conus, now without spiral course because of the absence of normal torsion, might by continued downward growth invade the common ventricle, dividing it sagittally into right and left parts; a wide interventricular defect would express the limit of this invasion by the septum. The aorta would arise from the right ventricle, the pulmonary trunk from the apparent left, and the two vessels would be of the same size. By this perfectly plausible sequence one type of crossed transposition might well be attained.

For the lesser degrees of transposition, those in which both aorta and pulmonary trunk arise from the right ventricle and in which the normal interventricular septum is more or less well marked, another theoretical explanation is required, for the presence of this septum in a nearly sagittal plane indicates that the ventricular and conal limbs are in the normal left-right relation of which the dextral spiral of the conus and truncus is a direct result. Here some actual detorsion must have occurred to bring about the changed relation of the two great vessels. Evidence of this detorsion in the aorta is supplied by the changing position of the coronary arteries in the different types. In searching for the cause for this detorsion certain facts seem to be of importance: early in their development some portions of the coiled heart tube become fixed in position, while other parts remain freely movable. The caudal wall of the common atrium is firmly attached to the diaphragm by the entering veins. The atrioventricular canal becomes more solid by the growth and fusion of the endocardial cushions, while the growth of the interventricular septum in the dorsal wall of interventricular passage fixes this section of the tube. The only region of the heart tube that now can move or be moved freely is the bulbar and conal section. Any detorsion must be exerted on this portion only.

The chief change in the bulbar region as it becomes the right ventricle is the outgrowth of the endothelial sinusoids. This outgrowth takes place chiefly at the sharpest convexity of the tube, and since in the normal embryonic heart of the fifth week the tip of the bulb points caudally, laterally and ventrally (Fig. 70, f), the chief growth of the sinusoids is normally in these directions (Fig. 73). The deep sinusoidal invasion causes the corresponding walls of the bulb to bulge and assume the shape of the right ventricle. The dorsal wall, in contrast, on which few if any sinusoids develop, remains relatively smooth and flat. The expanding chest wall readily accommodates the enlarging ventricle; the torsion of the bulbar limb is in no way affected.

If, taking advantage of its free and unattached condition, the bulb should so turn that its sharpest convexity points dorsally instead of ventrally, as is normal, the deepest growth of sinusoids would be dorsal and the ventricular wall would bulge in that direction. One embryo with this disposition of the sinusoids has been reported;[6] a reconstruction of its right ventricle and conus in contrast with that of a normal embryo of nearly the same age is given in Fig. 77, *b*. In this embryo the ventricular thrust would be dorsal, and would encounter the pulsating right atrium and the septum transversum, which at this period of development is almost vertically disposed, backed by the relatively solid liver. Meeting this, the heart itself as it expands must tend to be lifted forward. The whole heart cannot respond, however, for the atria, atrioventricular canal, and left ventricle are fixed; only the bulbar portion is free, as has already been pointed out. The walls of the interventricular canal may be expected, therefore, to serve as a hinge on which the forward movement of the bulb must pivot; the left wall will be held fast in place. This forward or ventral movement of the lower part of the bulb can be accomplished only by a rolling motion, or rotation around a vertical axis (Fig. 78). The lateral or right wall will be rolled forward, carrying with it the crista supraventricularis,

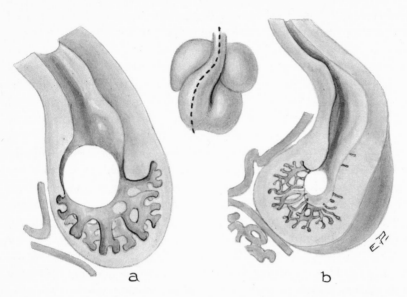

Fig. 77. (a) Reconstruction of the left half of the right ventricle and conus of a human embryo of 6.7 mm, 5 weeks, represented as though cut sagittally along the broken line in the smaller insert and viewed from the right side. The ventricular sinusoids sprout from the apex and from the ventral wall. (b) Similar view of the abnormal heart of a human embryo of 6.3 mm. The apex of the bulb points dorsally, abutting against the septum transversum and liver, and the sinusoids sprout chiefly in the same direction. This disposition of the sinusoids, if continued, may cause transposition of the great vessels. [From J. L. Bremer, *Arch. Path. 34*, 1023 (1942).]

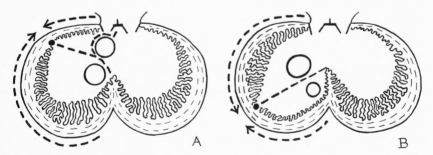

Fig. 78. Diagrams to show effect on aorta and pulmonary artery of the position of sinusoidal growth. Further explanation in text.

and this rotary motion in a sinistral direction will be transmitted upward to the common aortic-pulmonary trunk, thus tending to unwind the normal dextral spiral of that portion.

The degree of detorsion must depend on the relative number and depth of the sinusoids on the dorsal and lateral walls, and this again may be determined by the form of the embryonic heart. In the abnormal heart shown in Fig. 77, *b,* it is quite possible to imagine that further growth of the sinusoids dorsally would lift the end of the bulb so far away from the septum transversum that its apex would point caudally and then ventrally. Further growth of sinusoids would then be transferred to the ventral wall, inhibited on the dorsal wall; the original process would have proved self-limited. The timing or even the existence of this self-limitation might be reflected in the different types of transposition. The last sequence of cause and effect could lead to crossed transposition by the loss of the original interventricular septum. Perhaps the high percentage of crossed transposition may be due to the fact that this condition can be attained by two methods, one through the detorsion just described, showing the remains of the ventral septum and with pulmonary stenosis carried over from the lesser grades, and the other from the previously described sagittaly disposed ventricle and bulb (Fig. 70, *d*), with no torsion and with the great vessels of equal caliber. However, with all these theories it may still be said that the ultimate cause of the transposition of the great vessels of the heart is as yet unknown. All types seem to be derived from chance variations in the shape of the growing heart tube in a constricted space.

A syndrome comprising various forms of transposition of the great vessels with agenesis of the spleen and other malformations is gaining recognition.[7]

11 ——

DEVELOPMENT OF THE AORTIC ARCHES

Normal Pattern and Anomalies

Coarctation of the Aorta

When the anterior and the two lateral heart primordia have been rolled under the projecting head to form the single heart (p. 128), the truncus arteriosus lies almost directly beneath the first pair of pharyngeal pouches. The paired first aortic arches, derived from the original capillary plexus of this region (Fig. 79), run forward from the truncus, turn dorsally in front of each first pouch, and continue caudally as the paired dorsal aortae. Caudally from the truncus, in the tissue between the floor of the pharynx and the pericardial cavity on each side, extend the paired plexiform ventral aortae. As the head and pharynx continue their forward growth and successive pharyngeal pouches appear, capillary sprouts from the lengthening ventral aortae grow dorsally between pouches to meet similar sprouts from the dorsal aortae and together form new arches (Fig. 80). The heart, meanwhile, remains in its former position and its truncus moves caudally along the ventral aortae, an increasing portion of which thus appears cranial to it. In this seemingly caudal migration, the truncus lags appreciably behind the formation of new arches, so that there is always at least one new arch pair caudal to the truncus mouth. Four pairs of aortic arches are thus formed, one behind each pharyngeal pouch, which with the original first pair make five in all (Fig. 81). The ventral aortae over which the mouth of the truncus has last passed in its caudal

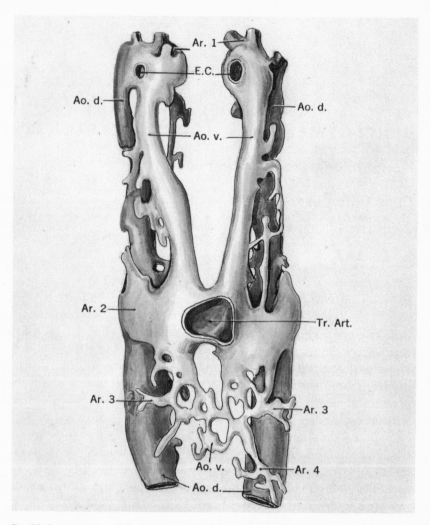

Fig. 79. Reconstruction of the blood vessels of the head of a rabbit embryo of 10 days, seen from the ventral side; the heart is removed by cutting the truncus arteriosus. Compare with Fig. 64. Ao.d, Ao.v, dorsal and ventral aortae; Ar. 1, 2, 3, 4, aortic arches; E.C., external carotid arteries, cut; Tr. art., truncus arteriosus. [From original of Fig. 8, J. L. Bremer, *Am. J. Anat.* 13, 124 (1912).]

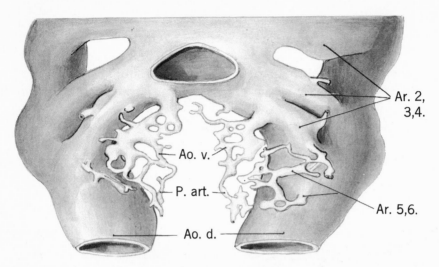

Fig. 80. Reconstruction of vessels in rabbit embryo of 10½ days. Orientation and lettering as in Fig. 79. Also, *P.art.*, extension of ventral plexus as pulmonary arteries. Note relation of fifth and pulmonary arches and the present origin of pulmonary arteries from fourth arches. [From original of Fig. 9, J. L. Bremer, Am. J. Anat. *13*, 125 (1912).]

migration either remain conjoined as a single sac, the aortic sac,[1] or are reseparated into the original paired structures (Fig. 82, *b, a*). Separation is the more usual condition, and from this form the most common, or normal, disposition of the branches of the permanent arch of the aorta is derived. The sac type permits the formation of some of the more unusual branch patterns.

In addition to these five well-defined vessel pairs, however, there is often, in embryos of about 6 weeks, a capillary plexus between the last two aortic arches on one or both sides. The plexus may soon take the form of a small artery joining the two arches, of a loop on one arch or the other, or of a branch running from the center of an arch to either ventral or dorsal aorta. In man a complete arch is never formed, yet these irregular fragments, which rarely persist more than a day or two, were considered by some anatomists as evidence of another pair of arches, the fifth, making the permanent last arches the sixth in the series. The importance of this interpolated arch is associated with the problem of the ultimobranchial body (p. 20); if this is a separate pouch, instead of a branch of the fourth pouch, it should be provided with a separate aortic arch, which thus seemed to have been found. The practical result of the discovery of the extra arch seems to have been chiefly a confusion in the nomenclature of the arches, the last pair being called V in the older books and VI in the more recent ones. For the sake of clarity it is well to speak of this last pair as the pulmonary arches, indicating their chief future relation.

Strictly speaking, each pulmonary arch joins the side of the homolateral ventral aorta some distance caudal to the mouth of the truncus (Fig. 81, *c, d*), and although the new transverse vessel and the proximal portion of the ventral aorta grow large together and

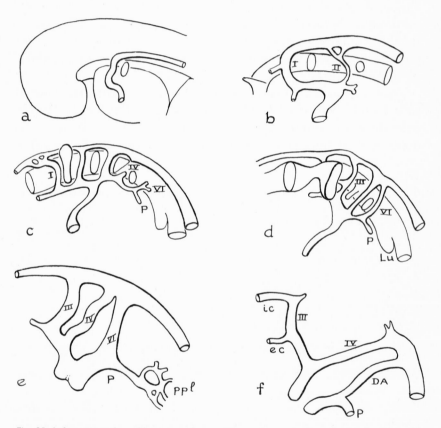

Fig. 81. Left aortic arches of human embryos of increasing ages, showing the development of the adult pattern (in part after Congdon): (a) 2 mm; (c) 4 mm; (f) 13.5 mm. The aortic arches are numbered. *DA,* ductus arteriosus; *ec, ic,* external and internal carotid arteries; *Lu,* lung; *p,* pulmonary artery; *ppl,* pulmonary plexus.

appear as a continuous arch of which the distal end of the ventral aorta seems merely a branch, actually the true arch comprises only the ductus arteriosus, and is normally obliterated at birth. In the anomalous absence of one of the pulmonary arches, the pulmonary artery of that side appears as the branch of the fourth arch, a condition occasionally encountered. The obliteration of the ductus is accomplished partly by the nerve-controlled contraction of the strong circular musculature,[2, 3] partly by the growth of elastic fibers in the subendothelial cushions which bulge into the lumen;[4] the combination of these two forces closes the lumen gradually, and this closure is followed by the fibrous degeneration of the vessel walls, resulting in the persistent ligamentum arteriosum. Not infrequently the ductus may remain open, either widely or enough to permit the passage of a pencil or a probe; these cases can now be successfully treated by surgery.[5, 6]

As the head of the embryo grows longer, both ventral and dorsal aortae send branches cranially into it, and since the dorsal branches are sufficiently supplied by the third pair of arches, the now unnecessary first and second pairs shrink and degenerate (Fig. 81, *d, e*).

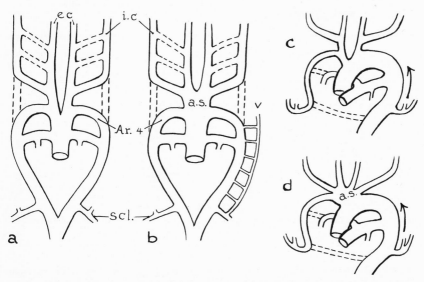

Fig. 82. Diagrams to show the changes in the aortic arches and in the ventral aorta without (*a, c,*) and with (*b, d*) the aortic sac *a.s.* Ar. 4, aortic arch; *e.c.*, external, and *i.c.*, internal carotid arteries; *scl.*, subclavian arteries; *v.*, vertebral artery.

Later, the growing head turns ventrally, making a sharp bend (the neck bend) in the region of the third and fourth arches, and the two pairs of arches respond, like the pouches between which they run (p. 18), by being crowded together ventrally and spread apart dorsally. The section of the dorsal aorta on each side between the third and fourth arches is accordingly made useless and normally disappears (*f*). With the loss of this section of the dorsal aortae, blood flows to the head either by the extended ventral aortae (external carotid arteries) or through the third arches to the cranial portions of the dorsal aortae (internal carotid arteries), while the sections of the ventral aortae between the third and fourth arches become the common carotid arteries. Caudally the blood passes by both the fourth and pulmonary arches to the body below.

During the changes that the symmetrically arranged embryonic aortic arches undergo in producing the adult aortic arch and its branches, the heart itself continues its caudal migration. The atria of the heart are firmly attached by the main entering veins, the inferior and superior cavae, to the septum transversum through which the veins pass. The septum becomes the central tendon of the diaphragm and as this moves caudally the heart must follow. The extent of this migration may be realized by considering that at the time when the first arch only is present the septum lies roughly at the level of the upper cervical vertebrae; in the adult the central tendon is in the same plane as the ensiform cartilage. This great migration caudally is due to the forward growth of the head and the development of the thoracic wall. The heart, meanwhile, has increased in size so that the migration of the truncus is somwhat less extensive, but still it is far removed from the pharyngeal pouches between which the arches originally ran. The branches of the aortic arches must lengthen considerably to retain their former relations with the pouches and other neighboring structures. At the same time, since in the dextrally coiled heart the conus and truncus run from the right ventricle toward the mid-line between the two atria, this terminal portion of the heart points to the left, and by this course favors the left members of the fourth and pulmonary arch pairs, which thus increase in size at the expense of the right members.

Additional changes also affect the arrangements of the branches of the adult arch. The vertebral arteries are formed by the longitudinal anastomoses of the first seven intersegmental branches of the paired aortae (Fig. 82, *b*), and of these branches only the seventh is preserved on each side; this seventh is soon lengthened into the arm bud as the subclavian artery, of which the vertebral artery then appears to be a branch. The first intersegmental vessels originally arise at the level of the dorsal ends of the fourth arches, and the seventh pair a short distance above the union of the paired aortae to form the single dorsal aorta below. Below this union the intersegmental branches are preserved as intercostals and serve to anchor this part of the aorta in position, but above it the paired aortae are now free from dorsal attachment, and as the truncus continues its caudal migration the ventral ends of the fourth and pulmonary arches follow, carrying with them the free part of the formerly dorsal aorta, rolling it forward and downward until the truncus is nearly at the level of the junction of the two dorsal aorta. By this action a portion of the former left dorsal aorta is added to the embryonic left fourth arch to form the complete adult aortic arch. The root of the left subclavian vessel must also migrate individually along the aortic wall, or be pulled by its attachments above, for it finally appears normally above the ductus, reversing their original relations. The final steps in this change in the relative position of the ventral and dorsal aortae may take place after birth, for at birth the pulmonary arch (ductus arteriosus) often follows a dorsocaudal course, at four months the ductus points directly dorsally, and only later is the counter-clockwise rotation completed, as shown by the almost cranial course of the ligamentum arteriosum characteristic of the adult.

With these facts as a foundation it is now possible to understand and to use intelligently the diagrams of the aortic arches and their derivatives commonly given in books on anatomy in interpreting the various anomalies of the branches of the adult arch. The published diagrams are of two types, those representing the arches in attempted perspective, with the dorsal aortae behind and the truncus in front, and those projected on one plane, with truncus and ventral aortae central and dorsal aortae lateral. The latter, which are in many ways simpler, represent the conditions as in a broiled chicken, split down the back and the two sides turned laterally and forward. This is the type shown in Fig. 82. For the two possible conditions of the ventral aortae as they spring from the truncus without and with the aortic sac, two sets of diagrams are necessary (*a, c* and *b, d*).

In both sets the condition of situs solitus is presumed, derived from the normal embryonic position of the truncus, pointing diagonally upward and to the left, with the consequent enlargement of the left fourth and pulmonary arches as being more directly in the course of the stream, and the relegation of the right members of the pairs to the position of branches. The left fourth embryonic arch remains as the ventral part of the adult aortic arch. The ventral part of the left pulmonary arch, with the pulmonary artery proper, forms the adult left pulmonary artery, the dorsal half remaining till birth as the ductus arteriosus; on the right this dorsal portion, beyond the true pulmonary artery, degenerates from disuse and is lost before the eighth week. The point of union of the two dorsal aortae, now behind instead of below the heart, is pulled to the left by the enlarging left arches. The lower portion of the right aorta, being thus stretched and put at a disadvantage, normally drops out also, leaving its upper part as the proximal segment of the right subclavian artery; rarely, this lower portion remains as a tiny vessel joining this artery with the dorsal aorta caudal to the origin of the left subclavian artery and running dorsal to the oesophagus.

The normal order of the branches of the adult aortic arch and the more common variations of this order[7] are shown in Fig. 83, and are to be compared with the two possible embryonic conditions for interpretation. Many other variations have been recorded,[8] but they are usually combinations of those shown here or to be explained by the same principles. Normally the adult aortic arch has three branches, the innominate, the left common carotid, and the left subclavian arteries. The innominate represents the ventral portion of the right fourth arch, much smaller than the left; it bifurcates, after a shorter or longer course, into the right subclavian and the right common carotid arteries. The right subclavian artery is composed successively of the remainder of the right fourth arch, the right dorsal aorta, and the right subclavian vessel proper, with the right vertebral artery as a branch. Its originally crooked course has been straightened by the descent of the heart. The right common carotid artery represents the right ventral aorta between the fourth and third arches; its continuation, the right external carotid, is the continuation of the ventral aorta forward. The right internal carotid artery incorporates the right third arch as its proximal portion and continues forward as the right dorsal aorta. Both carotid vessels send terminal growths toward the head. The left common carotid and its two branches are of similar embryonic origin to their counterparts on the right. The left subclavian artery and its upward migration have already been described. (The terms "internal" and "external" as applied to the carotid arteries as shown in Fig. 83 seem reversed until one realizes that, in such a diagram, lateral is actually dorsal, and that the internal carotid artery actually runs dorsal to the external as it enters the head.)

The normal disposition of the aortic arch branches, just described, is derived from the most common embryonic condition, that in which the ventral aortae have reseparated after the passage of the truncus. The most common variation of the branches of the arch (Fig. 83, *b*) comes from the aortic sac. The innominate and left common carotid arteries—in other words, both ventral aortae— and the right fourth arch are fused ventrally into a single trunk, called the *brachiocephalic trunk,* after a similar vessel that is normal in some animals. The left subclavian remains as a separate branch. Similar fusion of right and left ventral aortae (aortic sac) is found in Fig. 83, *c, d,* and *f,* but in each some further variation is added.

In Fig. 83, *c,* the left vertebral artery leaves the arch as a separate branch between the brachiocephalic trunk and the left subclavian artery. If one remembers that the vertebral artery arises as the terminal anastomoses of the first seven intervertebral branches of the aorta, the last of which also is prolonged as the subclavian vessel, it is easy to see that, if the terminal anastomosis fails to extend beyond the sixth intersegmental branch, the vertebral artery, making use of this vessel as a root, leaves the aorta at a higher level than the subclavian and will appear ventral to it on the aortic arch, as in this case. In Fig. 83, *f* the vertebral artery arises from the arch distal to the left subclavian artery. It is possible that this variation, the rarest of the series, may be due to an unusual three-dimensional character of the terminal intersegmental plexus, through which a longitudinal pathway was chosen for the vertebral artery dorsal to the subclavian root, utilizing perhaps the eighth intersegmental vessel as its root, and thus becoming the last, most dorsal branch of the arch.

Figure 83, *d,* shows the condition known as the *low origin* of the *right subclavian artery:* the lower portion of the right dorsal aorta, from the root of the right subclavian artery to the junction of the two aortae, a section that normally disappears or, rarely, remains as a tiny vessel, has in this case persisted and become the anomalous proximal section of the right subclavian. At the same time the right fourth arch beyond the right common carotid artery and the right dorsal aorta below it down to the root of the right subclavian artery have been obliterated. The figure also shows the brachio-cephalic trunk, derived from the aortic sac, but this is an unrelated variation and not essential. Later the point of union of the dorsal aortae (the apparent root of this low right subclavian artery) is carried

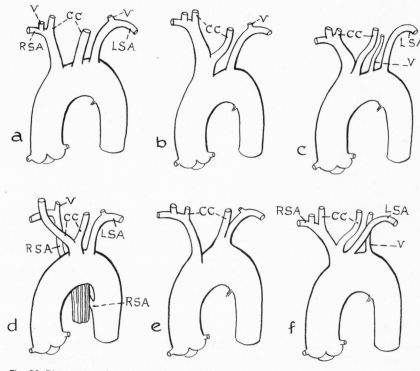

Fig. 83. Diagrams to show the relation of the branches of the aortic arch in normal disposition (a) and in the more common variations in order of rarity (slightly altered from De Garis). *CC,* common carotid artery; *LSA, RSA,* left and right subclavian artery; *V,* vetebral artery.

relatively higher by the rolling forward of the left dorsal aorta to form part of the arch (Fig. 84, a).

This anomalous right subclavian artery, since its root is the right dorsal aorta, should pass dorsal to the oesophagus, often indenting it obliquely, and that is the course followed in the great majority of cases (Fig. 84, a, b). In some 15 percent of such cases, however, it is found between the oesophagus and trachea (c), and in some others in front of the trachea. There is as yet no generally accepted explanation for this more ventral position of this vessel. Two suggestions have been offered, but objections have been raised to both: first[9] that the subclavian trunk behind the oesophagus becomes connected with the capillary plexus encircling and supplying

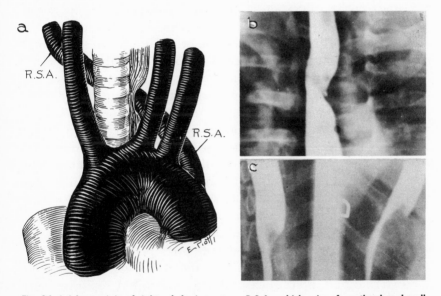

Fig. 84. (a) Low origin of right subclavian artery, R.S.A., which arises from the dorsal wall of the aortic arch and presses on the posterior wall of the esophagus. [(From Gross and Ware,) Surg., Gynec. & Obst. 83, 441 (1946.*] (b) Roentgenogram in left anterior-oblique projection showing oblique filling defect in dorsal wall of barium-filled oesophagus caused by pressure of anomalous right subclavian artery. [From E. B. D. Neuhauser, Am. J. Roentgenol. and Radium Therapy 56, 9 (1946).] (c) Adult male. Roentgenograms, antero-posterior and lateral projections, showing oblique defect on ventral wall of barium-filled oesophagus, indicating passage of anomalous right subclavian artery between trachea and esophagus. [From E. B. D. Neuhauser, Am. J. Roentgenol. and Radium Therapy 56, 11 (1946), kindness of Drs. Copleman and Robb.]

* By permission of Surgery, Gynecology and Obstetrics.

that tube, or at a higher level encircling the trachea as well, and through this plexus makes a new channel ventral to the oesophagus; and second,[10] that the two fifth arches persist and, freed in some way from the ventral aortic trunk and joining end to end as a single vessel in front of the trachea or oesophagus, become the proximal end of the right subclavian artery. The first suggestion seems the more reasonable.

In Fig. 83, *e,* derived from the normal embryonic condition without the aortic sac, the innominate artery seems to be matched by another similar though shorter vessel on the left side, carrying the left common carotid and subclavian vessels as branches. The left subclavian artery in its upward migration has met and slightly fused with the left common carotid artery. This probably indicates that the upward migration of this left subclavian along the dorsal aorta was greater than usual, perhaps with the added lift that the subclavian vessel used as its root one of the upper intersegmental vessels, the fifth or sixth, in place of the usual seventh.

Much more rarely other anomalies of arrangement of the branches of the arch are encountered, indicating earlier and more fundamental changes in the embryonic development. With the total agenesis of the right pulmonary arch, the pulmonary artery of that side becomes a branch of the proximal portion of the right sub-clavian artery, the former right fourth arch (p. 173). In other cases the dorsal aorta between the third and fourth arches, normally lost early, may persist on one or both sides as one of the rarest anom-alies. This condition is accompanied, and probably caused, by the agenesis or early degeneration of the corresponding third arch, for only in its absence would the dorsal aorta persist in spite of the long curved course forced upon it by the neck bend. In these cases the external and internal carotid arteries arise by separate roots directly from the arch if on the left side, from the innominate and subclavian artery if on the right. The agenesis of an arch inherent in both these types of anomaly can be explained as due to the failure of the two original capillary plexuses, from ventral and dorsal aortae, to meet and fuse in the mesenchyma between pharyngeal pouches. Later blocking and degeneration of the arch may be due to some chance kink in the easily flexible embryonic capiliform vessels.

The right fourth aortic arch may be predominant instead of the normal left arch. This is to be expected in situs inversus cordis, and in this case the branches of the arch are either in reversed sequence (mirror image) or may display any one of the anomalies just described in reverse. The dorsal aorta runs in the right paravertebral gutter. On the other hand, the right arch may be predominant in situs solitus of the heart, either as the larger member of a double aortic arch, in which both fourth arches persist intact (Fig. 85, *a*) or as the only remaining member of the pair (Figs. 85, *b;* 86, *a*). Yet even in these latter types signs of an earlier left arch are often revealed by the position of the descending aorta in the left paravertebral gutter or at least tending toward the left side before turning to the right, and by the persistence of portions of the left fourth arch. If the left common carotid artery arises as one of the first branches of the right arch (Fig. 85, *b*), its proximal segment, crossing ventral to the trachea, can be recognized as such a persisting portion of the left arch; and in Fig. 86, *a*, the similar left common carotid and the diverticulum of the right arch bearing the left subclavian artery together represent remaining parts of the left arch of Fig. 85, *a*, as though the arch had been interrupted between its two branches. In both these cases the constricting ring about the trachea and oesophagus is completed by the ligamentum arteriosum and the right pulmonary artery. Other types of arch anomaly, not yet recorded, but still possible, in man, are found in the offspring of rats with vitamin A[11] or folic acid[12] deficiency. In the great majority of cases of double aortic arch the trachea and oesophagus pass through the vascular ring; the few cases reported in which the smaller right aorta runs ventral to the trachea or oesophagus, are, perhaps, similar to those in which the low right subclavian artery takes the same course, and equally unexplained except by the same suggested theories—that the course of the dorsal aorta has been diverted either through a peritracheal and perioesophageal vascular plexus or into persistent fifth arches. The vascular ring may be large enough to accommodate easily these hollow tubes or so small as to have a constricting action, with symptoms of stridor or dysphagia. These same symptoms can be induced also by any other sufficient pressure on these tubular organs, as, for instance, pressure of the partial vascular ring caused

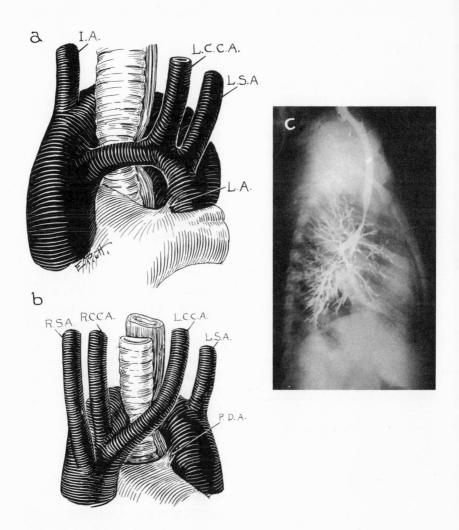

Fig. 85. (a) Double aortic arch, forming ring around trachea and oesophagus. Right arch dominant. [From Gross and Ware, *Surg., Gynec. & Obstet. 83*, 439 (1946).*] (b) Right arch, with left common carotid artery arising on right and nearly completing the constricting ring. *I.A.,* innominate artery; *L.A.,* ligamentum arteriosum; *L.C.C.A., R.C.C.A.,* common carotid arteries; *L.S.A., R.S.A.,* subclavian arteries; *P.D.A.,* patent ductus arteriosus. [From Gross and Ware, *Surg. Gynec. & Obstet. 83*, 437 (1946).*] (c) Infant. Lateral roentgenogram of the chest following instillation of lipiodol. There is marked narrowing of the treachea in all diameters just above the bifurcation at the level of the aortic arches. [From E. B. D. Neuhauser, *Am. J. Roentgenol. and Radium Therapy 56*, 5 (1946).]

by a right subclavian artery of low origin from a normal left aortic arch, by the anomalous left common carotid artery as the first branch of the right aortic arch, or by the persistence of the left ductus arteriosus with a right aortic arch. These various pressures can now be recognized and distinguished with surprising accuracy by roentgen diagnosis,[13] the transverse path of the right member of the aortic ring (Fig. 85, *a*) being differentiated from the diagonal path of the anomalous origin of the right subclavian artery (Fig. 84, *b*) by the shape and direction of the dorsal indentations in the barium-filled oesophagus. Even the rare occurrence of the anomalous right subclavian artery passing ventral to the oesophagus has been recognized by this method (Fig. 84, *c*). Fortunately surgery[14] for the relief of the symptoms due to these anomalies of the embryonic arch system is now available in certain cases. The anomalies of the pulmonary arteries have been described in the chapter on lung (p. 41).

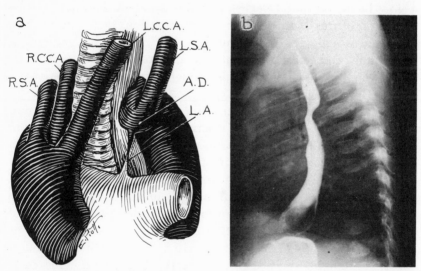

Fig. 86. (*a*) Right aortic arch, with proximal section of left common carotid artery and aortic diverticulum A.D. on left representing the two ends of the incomplete left arch. Ring about trachea and oesophagus is made tighter by the ligamentum arteriosum and the right pulmonary artery. Lettering as in Fig. 85. [From Gross and Ware, *Surg., Gynec. & Obstet. 83*, 437 (1946).*] (*b*) Infant. Lateral roentgenogram of chest with barium-filled oesophagus; large rounded posterior defect produced by the right aortic arch is clearly seen, and ventrally the three defects may represent pressure by L.C.C.A., A.D., and the pulmonary artery, successively. [From E. B. D. Neuhauser, *Am. J. Roentgenol. and Radium Therapy 56*, 3 (1946).]

Coarctation of the aorta, the local narrowing of the aortic arch just as it turns downward to become the descending aorta, has been recognized for many years, and the accompanying compensatory enlargement of the collateral circulation, on the completeness of which in extreme cases continuation of life depends, is well understood. The narrowing may occur chiefly in one of two forms,[15] known as Type I, the congenital or fetal form, and Type II, the adult form, respectively, so called from the period of life in which each type is most frequently encountered. In the fetal type the lesion is in the form of a more or less severe local stenosis, fusiform in shape, in the region known as the aortic isthmus, situated between the root of the left subclavian artery and the entrance of the ductus arteriosus (Fig. 87, *a*). This is a supposedly "stagnant" segment of the fetal aorta, between the aortic blood stream supplying the head and arms and the ductal stream to the body and legs, and a slight narrowing of the aorta at this point is normally present before birth; postnatal persistence of this narrowing after the obliteration of the ductus constitutes coarctation. In the adult type the stenosis is always in the immediate vicinity of the ligamentum arteriosum, and consists of an abrupt indentation of the aortic wall, mostly on the distal surface, as though it were constricted by a tightly drawn cord; often this constriction is extended within the lumen as a perforated diaphram (Fig. 87, *e, f*). This conformation may be due either to simple traction on the aortic wall by the degenerating and shrinking ductus arteriosus or to the extension to the aortic wall of the obliterative processes active in the ductus in the form of a narrow encircling ring.

The two types of coarctation seem definite, and an apparently adequate explanation of each type is at hand. Yet some cases of coarctation do not fall into either category; anatomically fetal or neonatal types are found (or noticed first) in adults, and adult forms in infants. These are grouped as Type III. Also in a few cases the subclavian artery or the separate root of the left vertebral artery arises from the aorta distal to the coarctation or from the coarctation itself (Fig. 87, *b, c, f*), and these and all other irregular forms are grouped in Type IV. The individual origin of the vertebral artery has already been explained as a simple variation of its intervertebral roots, and the position of the subclavian artery in these cases is readily understood as due to the retardation of its normal cranial migration along the aortic wall; but the presence of coarctation above the subclavian branch seems to invalidate the "stagnant isthmus" theory as an adequate explanation for Type I cases.

In all probability the cause of coarctation, of whatever type and wherever found, is the same degenerative obliteration of a previously active branch vessel as is responsible for this condition in Type II.[16] The aortic isthmus is matched embryologically by the less well known right subclavian isthmus, situated a short distance along that artery beyond its origin from the innominate trunk; this proximal portion of the subclavian represents the right fourth aortic arch. On both sides the presenting degenerating vessel, at about 6 or 7 weeks, is that section of the dorsal aorta between the third and fourth arches (Fig. 88). As in the case of the postnatally degenerating ductus in Type II, the obliterative processes of these

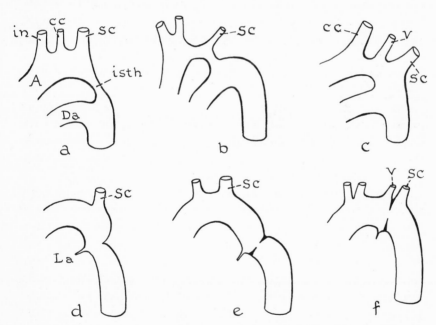

Fig. 87. Various types of coarctation of the aorta (after Bonnet). (a) Type I (fetal), with variations in (b) and (c); (d) Type II (adult), with (e) and (f) as variations. cc, common carotid artery; Da, ductus arteriosus; in, innominate; isth, isthmus; sc, left subclavian artery; v, vertebral.

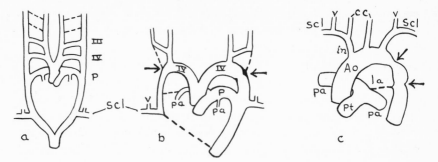

Fig. 88. Diagrams of the aortic arches in the fifth and seventh weeks and in the newborn: (a) loss of arches I and II; (b) loss of dorsal aortae between arches III and IV, and of the dorsal portion of right arch VI; (c) loss of right dorsal aorta below the subclavian artery and closure of the ductus arteriosus. Changes in the relative positions of the component parts due to differential growth rate can be followed, as well as the cranial migration of the root of the left subclavian artery. Arrows point to known sites of coarctation. Lettering as before, and la, ligamentum arteriosum.

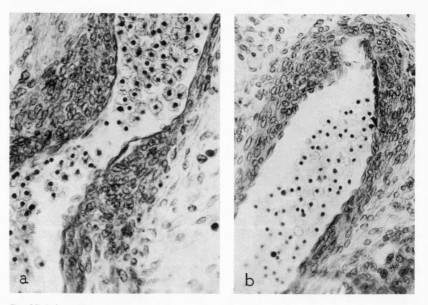

Fig. 89. Isthmus formation in rat embryos of seven weeks. (a) Sagittal section through right isthmus; the right common carotid artery lies above, the right fourth arch (right subclavian artery) below. The proximal portion of this arch innominate artery lies in other sections. The wall of the arch is thickened and the lumen narrowed at the site of the former junction with the now obliterated section of dorsal aorta. (b) Transverse section through left arch IV, showing at top the last remaining lumen of the degenerating section of the dorsal aorta (cf. Fig. 81, f); note thickening of wall of arch IV and local narrowing of lumen. [From J. L. Bremer, Arch. Path. 45, 429 (1952).]

two sections of the dorsal aortae may extend onto and around the caudal ends of the two fourth arches in the form of a slight local endothelial thickening and a more noticeable increase of constricting musculature, with consequent narrowing of the lumen. The constriction is much less sharp in these younger vessels, and the picture more fusiform. The two constrictions, of the right and left fourth arches respectively, are shown in Fig. 89, *a* and *b*.

On the right side the constrictive processes, which cause the isthmus, soon yield to the conterpressure of the increasingly more powerful force of the blood stream until at birth the subclavian isthmus is rarely noticeable. On the left, the aortic isthmus lies in the stagnant section of the descending aorta, and, according to the volume of the passing stream (for the term "stagnant" is only relative), may remain as a fairly open isthmus and expand fully at birth, or may become increasingly narrow or even close completely, unable to open after birth in spite of the suddenly increased blood stream. The coarctation is due to the stagnation of this section of the aorta acting on the already present isthmus; the isthmus itself depends on the normal degeneration of the embryonic dorsal aortae between the third and fourth aortic arches, and on the extension of this degenerative process to the dorsal ends of these arches.

There are other regions where vascular degeneration may theoretically spread to the adjoining aortae, at the distal end of the right sixth arch and at both ends of the lower segment of the right dorsal aorta. In fact, a thickening of the musculature is not infrequently seen at these points in the embryo, but since no isthmus formation accompanies them the narrowings soon disappear with the increasing blood flow, following the same fate as the subclavian coarctation, already mentioned.

Both main types of coarctation are thus caused by the extension to the aorta itself of the degenerative processes present in former branches newly obliterated. For the fetal type the disappearance of the sections of the dorsal aortae between the third and fourth arches is responsible; for the adult type the closure of the ductus arteriosus is the chief factor. Most of the variations of both types depend on the extent of the normal cranial migration of the left subclavian artery (Fig. 87, *a, b, c*) or less commonly on that of the vertebral artery (*c, f*).

REFERENCES

Chapter 1. The Respiratory and Alimentary Systems

1. J. P. Schaeffer, *The nose, paranasal sinuses, nasolacrimal passageways and olfactory organ in man* (Blakiston, Philadelphia, 1920).
2. I. Broman, "Das Organon vomero-nasale Jacobsoni, ein Wassergeruchsorgan!" *Anat. Hefte 58,* 137–191 (1920).
3. J. LeRoy Conel, "The origin of the neural crest," *J. Comp. Neurol. 76,* 191–215 (1942).
4. G. Politzer, "Die Grenzfurche des Oberkieferfortsatzes und die Tränennasenrinne," *Ztschr. f. Anat. u. Entwcklngsgesch. 105,* 329–332 (1936).
5. J. P. Schaeffer, "Genesis and development of the nasolacrimal passageways in man," *Am. J. Anat. 13,* 1–24 (1912).
6. J. V. Cassady, "Developmental anatomy of the nasolachrymal duct," *Arch. Ophth. 47,* 141–158 (1952).
7. J. D. Boyd, "The classification of the upper lip in mammals," *J. Anat. 67,* 409–416 (1933).
8. V. Veau and G. Politzer, "Embryologie du Bec-de-lièvre—le palais primaire," *Ann. d'anat. path. 13,* 275–326 (1936).
9. T. S. King, "The anatomy of hare-lip in man," *J. Anat. 88,* 1–12 (1954).
10. H. B. Adelmann, "The problem of cyclopia," *Quart. Rev. Biol. 11,* 161–182, 284–304 (1936).
11. C. R. Stockard, "The development of artificially produced cyclopean fish—'the magnesium embryo,'" *J. Exper. Zoöl. 6,* 285–337 (1909).
12. B. Orban, *Oral histology and embryology* (Mosby, St. Louis, 1949).
13. H. Sicher and L. Pohl, "Zur Entwicklung des menschlichen Unterkiefers," *Ztschr. f. Stomatol. 32,* 552–560 (1934).
14. J. G. Warbrick, J. R. McIntyre, and A. G. Ferguson, "Aetiology of congenital bilateral fistulae of the lower lip," *Brit. J. Plastic Surg. 4,* 254–262 (1952).
15. Frazier, C. H., and J. B. Alpers, "Adamantinoma of the cranio-pharyngeal duct," *Arch. Neurol. & Psychiat. 26,* 905–965 (1931).
16. C. L. Streeter, "Development of the auricle in the human embryo," *Carnegie Contrib. Embryol. 14,* 111–138 (1922).

Chapter 2. Pharynx and Neck

1. J. A. Hammar, "Das Schicksal der Zweiten Schlundspalte," *Arch. f. mikr. Anat. 61,* 404–458 (1903).
2. B. F. Kingsbury, "Fate of the ultimobranchial body within the thyroid gland," *Anat. Rec. 61,* 155–167 (1935).
3. G. L. Weller, "Development of the thyroid, parathyroid and thymus glands in man," *Carnegie Contrib. Embryol. 24,* 93–142 (1933).
4. B. M. Patten, *Human embryology* (Blakiston, Philadelphia, 1946).

REFERENCES

Chapter 3. Trachea, Bronchi, and Lungs

1. F. P. Gegenbach and E. J. Dobos, "Congenital tracheoesophageal fistula," *J. Pediat. 19*, 644–655 (1941).

2. G. W. Ware and L. L. Cross, "Congenital tracheo-esophageal fistula without atresia of the esophagus," *Pediatrics 14*, 254–258 (1954).

3. B. Bencke, "Ueber Bauchlunge und Hernia diaphragmatica spuria," *Verhandl. d. deutsch. Gesellsch. f. inn. Med. 9*, 201–211 (1905).

4. R. K. Brown and L. L. Robbins, "Bronchiogenic cysts of the mediastinum and lung," *J. Thoracic Surg. 13*, 84–105 (1944).

5. J. A. Hammar, "Ein Fall von Nebenlunge bei einem Menschenfötus von 11.7 mm.," *Beitr. z. path. Anat. 36*, 518–527 (1904).

6. D. V. Davies and F. W. Gunz, "Two cases of lower accessory lung . . . ," *J. Path. & Bact. 56*, 417–427 (1944).

7. N. L. Rusby and T. H. Sellors, "Congenital deficiency of pericardium associated with bronchogenic cyst," *Brit J. Surg. 32*, 357–364 (1945).

8. J. L. Bremer, "Accessory bronchi in embryos . . . ," *Anat. Rec. 54*, 361–374 (1932).

9. D. MacKinnon, "Tracheal diverticula," *J. Path. & Bact. 65*, 513–517 (1953).

10. L. B. Thomas and E. A. Boyden, "Agenesis of the right lung," *Surgery 31*, 429–435 (1952).

11. C. F. Ferguson and E. B. D. Neuhauser, "Congenital absence of the lung . . . ," *Am. J. Roentgenol. & Radium Therapy 56*, 459–471 (1944).

12. D. S. Lukas, C. T. Dotter, and I. Steinberg, "Agenesis of the lung and patent ductus arteriosus . . . ," *New England J. Med. 249*, 107–109 (1953).

13. J. L. Bremer, "The protoplasmic films of the fat cell . . . pulmonary alveolus . . . renal glomerulus," *Anat. Rec. 70*, 263–285 (1938).

14. F. N. Low, "Electron microscopy of the rat lung," *Anat. Rec. 113*, 437–449 (1952); "The pulmonary alveolar epithelium of laboratory mammals and man," *Anat. Rec. 117*, 241–263 (1953).

15. C. G. Loosli, "The structure of the respiratory portion of the mammalian lung," *Am. J. Anat. 62*, 375–425 (1938).

16. C. C. Macklin, "Pulmonary sumps, dust accumulations, alveolar fluid and lymph vessels," *Acta Anat. 23*, 1–33 (1955).

17. M. E. Davis and E. L. Potter, "Intrauterine respiration of the human fetus," *J.A.M.A. 131*, 1194–1201 (1946).

18. J. L. Bremer, "Postnatal development of alveoli in the mammalian lung . . . ," *Carnegie Contrib. Embryol. 25*, 85–110 (1935).

19. J. L. Bremer, "Fate of the remaining lung tissue after lobectomy or pneumonectomy," *J. Thoracic Surg. 6*, 334–342 (1937).

20. H. M. Higgins, "Present concepts of pathogenesis . . . of bronchiectasis," *Dis. of Chest 9*, 5–23 (1943).

21. R. Adams and E. D. Churchill, "Situs inversus, sinusitis bronchiectasis," *J. Thoracic Surg. 7*, 206–217 (1937).

22. G. E. Gruenfeld and S. H. Gray, "Malformations of the lung," *Arch. Path. 31*, 392–407 (1941).

23. J. Caffey, "On the natural regression of pulmonary cysts during early infancy," *Pediatrics 11* (1), 48–64 (1953).

24. R. P. Johnson, "Anomalous pulmonary vein," *Ann. Int. Med. 42* (1), 11–25 (1955).

25. Edwards, J. E., "Pathological and developmental considerations in anomalous pulmonary venous connection," *Proc. Staff Meetings Mayo Clinic 28,* 441-452 (1953).

26. H. C. Maier, "Absence or hypoplasia of a pulmonary artery with anomalous systemic arteries to the lung," *J. Thoracic Surg. 28,* 145-162 (1954).

27. D. M. Pryce, "Lower accessory pulmonary artery," *J. Path. & Bact. 58,* 457-467 (1946).

Chapter 4. Intestinal Tract

1. C. M. Jackson, "On the developmental topography of the thoracic and abdominal viscera," *Anat. Rec. 3,* 361-396 (1909).

2. J. L. Bremer, "Experiments on the aortic arches of the chick," *Anat. Rec. 37,* 225-254 (1928).

3. G. M. Wyburn, "Development of the infra-umbilical portion of the abdominal wall—ectopia vesicae," *J. Anat. 71,* 201-231 (1937).

4. O. Swensen, E. B. D. Neuhauser, and L. K. Peckett, "New concepts of the etiology . . . of Hirshsprung's disease," *Pediatrics 4,* 201-209 (1949).

5. J. L. Bremer, "Diverticula and duplications of the intestinal tract," *Arch. Path. 38,* 132-140 (1944).

6. F. T. Lewis and F. W. Thyng, "Regular occurrence of intestinal diverticula in embryos . . . ," *Am. J. Anat. 7,* 505-519 (1907).

7. F. P. Johnson, "Development of the mucous membrane of the oesophagus, stomach and small intestine in the human embryo," *Am. J. Anat. 10,* 521-561 (1910); "Development of the mucous membrane of the large intestine and vermiform process in the human embryo," *Am. J. Anat. 14,* 187-226 (1913).

8. A. W. Gray, "Triplication of the large intestine," *Arch. Path. 30,* 1215-1222 (1940).

9. B. A. E. Johns, "Developmental changes in the oesophageal epithelium in man," *J. Anat. 86* (4), 431-442 (1952).

10. R. E. Gross, E. B. D. Neuhauser, and L. A. Longino, "Thoracic diverticula which originate from the intestine," *Ann. Surg. 131,* 363-374 (1950).

11. J. L. Bremer, "Dorsal intestinal fistula . . . ," *Arch. Path. 54,* 132-138 (1952).

12. W. W. Keen and W. M. L. Coplin, "Sacrococcygeal tumor," *Surg., Gynec. & Obst. 3,* 662-671 (1906).

13. F. Lucksch, "Ueber Myeloschisis mit abnormer Darmansmundung," *Ztschr. f. Heilk. 24,* 143-156 (1903).

14. Lereboullet, quoted from Hertwig, *Ann. sci. nat. zool.* (4) *20* (1868).

15. C. Hertwig, "Urmund und Spina bifida," *Arch. f. mikr. Anat. 39,* 353-503 (1892).

16. G. M. H. Veeneklass, "Pathogenesis of intrathoracic gastrogenous cysts," *Am. J. Dis. Child. 33,* 500-507 (1952).

17. R. V. Herren and J. E. Edwards, "Diplomyelia (duplication of the spinal cord)," *Arch. Path. 30,* 1203-1214 (1940).

18. D. D. Matson, R. R. Woods, M. D. Campbell, and F. D. Ingraham, "Diastematomyelia (congenital clefts of the spinal cord)," *Pediatrics 6,* 98-112 (1950).

19. A. Barry, B. M. Patten, and B. H. Stewart, "Possible causative factors . . . Arnold-Chiari malformation," *Anat. Rec. 121,* 261 (1955); abstract.

REFERENCES

20. C. G. Smith, "Changes in length . . . of the spinal cord with changes in position . . . ," *Anat. Rec. 121,* 416 (1955); abstract.

21. W. E. Ladd and R. E. Gross, *Abdominal surgery in infancy and childhood* (Saunders, Philadelphia, 1941).

Chapter 5. Liver and Pancreas

1. Hans Elias, "A reexamination of the structure of the mammalian liver, I. Parenchymal architecture," *Am. J. Anat. 84,* 311–333 (1949); "II. Hepatic lobule . . . vascular and biliary systems," *ibid. 85,* 379–456 (1949).

2. C. S. Minot, "On a hitherto unrecognized form of blood circulation without capillaries . . . ," *Proc. Boston Soc. Nat. Hist. 29,* 185–215 (1900).

3. A. S. Begg, "The anomalous persistence in embryos of the peri-intestinal rings . . . vitelline veins," *Am. J. Anat. 13,* 103–110 (1912).

4. A. W. Chacko and S. R. M. Reynolds, "Development of the ductus venosus," *Anat. Rec. 115,* 151–173 (1953).

5. C. F. W. McClure and E. G. Butler, "The development of the vena cava inferior in man," *Am. J. Anat. 35,* 331–383 (1925).

6. G. G. Merrill, "Complete absence of the left lobe of the liver," *Arch. Path. 42,* 232–233 (1946).

7. W. E. Ladd and R. E. Gross, *Abdominal surgery in infancy and childhood* (Saunders, Philadelphia, 1941).

8. F. T. Lewis, "The development of the liver," in F. Keibel and F. P. Mall, eds., *Manual of human embryology* (Lippincott, Philadelphia, 1912), II, 403–428.

9. E. B. D. Neuhauser, M. Elkin, and B. Landing, "Congenital direct communication between biliary system and respiratory tract," *Am. J. Dis. Child. 83,* 654–659 (1952).

10. E. A. Boyden, "The sphincter of Oddi . . . ," *Surgery 1,* 25–37 (1937).

11. E. H. Ahrens, R. Harris, and H. E. McMahon, "Atresia of the intrahepatic bile ducts," *Pediatrics 8,* 628–647 (1951).

12. F. P. Johnson, "The development of the lobule of the pig's liver," *Am. J. Anat. 25,* 299–327 (1919).

13. F. C. Fishback, "Regeneration of the liver," *Arch. Path. 7,* 955–977 (1929).

14. G. Hellweg, "Congenital absence of intrahepatic venous system simulating Eck fistula," *Arch. Path. 57,* 425–430 (1954).

15. J. Hickman, J. E. Edwards, and F. C. Mann, "Venous anomalies in a dog," *Anat. Rec. 104,* 137–146 (1949).

16. P. N. B. Odgers, "Some observations of the development of the ventral pancreas in man," *J. Anat. 65,* 1–7 (1930).

17. R. R. Bensley, "Studies on the pancreas of the guinea pig," *Am. J. Anat. 12,* 297–388 (1911).

18. E. T. Thorsness, "An aberrant pancreatic nodule . . . neck of human gall bladder . . . ," *Anat. Rec. 77,* 319–333 (1940).

19. J. L. Bremer, "Pancreatic ducts and pancreatic bladders," *Am. J. Anat. 31,* 289–318 (1923).

20. E. A. Boyden, "The problem of the pancreatic bladder . . . ," *Am. J. Anat. 36,* 151–183 (1925).

21. E. A. Boyden, "A typical pancreatic bladder developed from an accessory pancreas," *Anat. Rec. 23,* 195–203 (1922).

22. S. Farber, "Pancreatic function and disease in early life, V," *Arch. Path. 37,* 238–252 (1944).

REFERENCES

Chapter 6. Urinary System and Suprarenal Gland

1. F. S. Winter, "Persistent left superior vena cava," *Angiology 5* (2), 90–132 (1954).
2. G. C. Huber, "On the development and shape of the uriniferous tubules . . . ," *Am. J. Anat. 4* (suppl.), 1–98 (1905).
3. J. Trueta, A. E. Barclay, P. M. Daniel, K. J. Franklin, and M. L. Prichard, *Studies of the renal circulation* (Charles C Thomas, Springfield, Illinois, 1947).
4. H. A. Kelly and C. F. Burnam, *Diseases of the kidneys, ureters and bladder* (Appleton, New York, 1922).
5. L. P. Wershub and T. J. Kirkwin, "Ureterocele, its etiology, pathogenesis and diagnosis," *Am. J. Surg. 88,* 317–327 (1954).
6. O. Swensen, H. E. MacMahan, W. E. Jacques, and J. S. Campbell, "A new concept of the etiology of megaloureter," *New England J. Med. 246,* 41–46 (1952).
7. J. L. Bremer, "Origin of the renal artery . . . ," *Am. J. Anat. 18,* 179–200 (1915).
8. O. F. Kampmeier, "Ueber der Schicksal der erstgeformten Harnkanalchen . . . ," *Arch. f. Anat. u. Physiol. Anat. Abt.,* pp. 204–226 (1919).
9. I. Gersh, "The correlation of structure and function in the developing mesonephros and metanephros," *Carnegie Contrib. Embryol. 26,* 33–58 (1937).
10. J. L. Bremer, "The interrelations of the mesonephros, kidney and placenta . . . ," *Am. J. Anat. 19,* 179–205 (1916).
11. Interesting articles and discussions on the physiological aspects of this question will be found in the *Cold Spring Harbor Symposia on Quantitative Biology,* vol. 19 (1954).
12. K. Benirschke and D. G. McKay, "The antiduretic hormone in fetus and infant," *Obst. & Gynec. 1,* 638–649 (1953).
13. W. M. Davidson and G. I. M. Ross, "Bilateral absence of the kidneys and related congenital anomalies," *J. Path. & Bact. 68* (2), 459–474 (1954).
14. R. Chwalla, "Entwicklung der Harnblase . . . ," *Ztschr. f. Anat. u. Entwcklngsgesch. 83,* 615–733 (1927).
15. W. E. Ladd and R. E. Gross, *Abdominal surgery in infancy and childhood* (Saunders, Philadelphia, 1941).
16. M. F. L. Keene and E. E. Hewer, "The development of the human suprarenal gland," *J. Anat. 61,* 302–324 (1927).
17. U. U. Uotila, "Development of the fetal and permanent adrenal cortex in man," *Anat. Rec. 76,* 183–203 (1940).
18. R. E. Gross, "Neoplasms producing endocrine disturbances in childhood," *Am. J. Dis. Child. 59,* 579–628 (1940).
19. D. M. Angevine, "Pathological anatomy of hypophysis and adrenals in anencephaly," *Arch. Path. 26,* 507–518 (1938).
20. E. Zuckerkandl, "The development of the chromaffin organs and of the suprarenal gland," in F. Keibel and F. P. Mall, eds., *Manual of human embryology* (Lippincott, Philadelphia, 1912), II, 157–179.

Chapter 7. Uterus and Vagina, Genital Apparatus, and External Genitalia

1. P. T. Buerger and H. E. Petzing, "Congenital cysts of the corpus uteri," *Am. J. Obst. & Gynec. 67,* 143–151 (1954).

REFERENCES

2. R. H. Hunter, "Observations on the development of the female genital tract," *Carnegie Contrib. Embryol. 22*, 91–108 (1930).

3. W. A. Mijsberg, "Ueber die Entwicklung der Vagina und des Sinus urogenitalis beim Menschen," *Ztschr. f. Anat. u. Entwcklngsges. 74*, 684–760 (1924).

4. A. K. Koff. "Development of the vagina in the female fetus," *Carnegie Contrib. Embryol. 24*, 59–91 (1933).

5. Erna Vilas, "Ueber die Entwicklung der menschlichen Scheide," *Ztschr. f. Anat. u. Entwcklngsges. 98*, 263–292 (1932).

6. D. G. McKay, A. T. Hertig, E. C. Adams, and S. Danziger, "Histochemical observations on the germ cells of human embryos," *Anat. Rec. 117*, 201–220 (1953).

7. A. D. Chiquoine, "Identification, origin and migration of the primordial germ cells," *Anat. Rec. 110*, 135–146 (1954).

8. E. Witschi, "Migration of the germ cells of human embryos from the yolk sac to the primitive gonadal folds," *Carnegie Contrib. Embryol. 32*, 69–80 (1948).

9. J. M. Essenberg, M. Horowitz, S. Davidson, and V. L. Ryder, "Further studies of the germ cell problem," *Anat. Rec. 121*, 393 (1955); abstract.

10. J. L. Bremer, "Morphology of the tubules of the human testis and epididymis," *Am. J. Anat. 11*, 393–411 (1911).

11. O. S. Lowsley, "Development of the human prostate gland . . . ," *Am. J. Anat. 13*, 299–349 (1912).

12. G. B. Wislocki and A. F. Guttmacher, "Spontaneous peristalsis of the excised whole uterus and Fallopian tubes . . . ," *Bull. Johns Hopkins Hosp. 35*, 246–252 (1924).

13. T. A. Rodenberg and A. V. Postoloff, "Lithopedion . . . two cases presenting as rectal lesions," *Am. J. Surg. 87*, 898–901 (1954).

14. O. F. Kampmeier, "On the problem of 'parthenogenesis' in the mammalian ovary," *Am. J. Anat. 43*, 45–76 (1929).

15. R. B. Tunney and R. E. Hunter, "Inguinal ectopia of ovary, tube, uterus," *New England J. Med. 242*, 1011–1012 (1950).

16. A. Jost, "Recherches sur les corrélations endocrines dans le développement foetal," *Bull. Soc. Fribourg. des sci. nat. 40*, 130–140 (1950).

17. G. M. Wyburn, "Development of the infra-umbilical portion of the abdominal wall—ectopia vesicae," *J. Anat. 71*, 201–231 (1937).

18. M. H. Spaulding, "Development of the external genitalia in the human embryo," *Carnegie Contrib. Embryol. 13*, 67–88 (1921).

19. B. M. Patten and A. Barry, "Genesis of exstrophy of the bladder and epispadias," *Am. J. Anat. 90*, 35–57 (1952).

20. R. E. Gross and T. C. Moore, "Duplication of the urethra," *Arch. Surg. 60*, 749–761 (1950).

Chapter 8. Heart, I

1. A. T. Hertig, "Angiogenesis in the early human chorion . . . ," *Carnegie Contrib. Embryol. 25*, 37–82 (1935).

2. J. L. Bremer, "The earliest blood vessels in man," *Am. J. Anat. 16*, 447–475 (1914).

3. J. L. Bremer, "The development of the aorta and aortic arches in rabbits," *Am. J. Anat. 13*, 111–128 (1912).

4. C. L. Davis, "Development of the human heart . . . to . . . embryos of 20 paired somites," *Carnegie Contrib. Embryol. 19*, 247–284 (1927).

5. B. M. Patten and T. C. Kramer, "Initiation of contraction in the embryonic chick heart," *Am. J. Anat. 53,* 349–375 (1933).

6. B. M. Patten, "Initiation and early changes in the character of the heart beat in vertebrate embryos," *Physiol. Rev. 29,* 31–47 (1949).

7. M. R. Lewis, "Development of cross striation in heart muscle—chick," *Bull. Johns Hopkins Hosp. 30,* 176–181 (1919).

8. C. M. Goss, "The first contractions of the heart in rat embryos," *Anat. Rec. 70,* 505–524 (1938).

9. J. L. Bremer, "Presence and influence of two spiral streams in the heart . . . ," *Am. J. Anat. 49,* 409–440 (1932).

10. K. Goerttler, "Ueber Blutstromwirkung als Gestaltungsfaktor für die Entwicklung des Herzens," *Beitr. pathol. Anat. u. allgem. Pathol. 115,* 33–56 (1955).

11. A. Keith and M. Flack, "The muscular connections between the primary divisions of the vertebrate heart," *J. Anat. & Physiol. 41,* 172–189 (1907).

12. L. M. DeWitt, "Observations on the sino-ventricular connecting system . . . heart," *Anat. Rec. 3,* 475–497 (1909).

13. A. Muir, "The development of the ventricular part of the conducting tissue in the heart . . . sheep," *J. Anat. 88,* 381–389 (1954).

14. A. Keith, "The Hunterian Lectures on the malformations of the heart," *Lancet 2,* 359, 433, 519 (1909).

Chapter 9. Heart, II. Septation

1. C. V. Morrill, "On the development of the atrial septum . . . of the pig embryo," *Am. J. Anat. 20,* 351–373 (1916).

2. B. M. Patten, "Developmental defects at the foramen ovale," *Am. J. Path. 14,* 135–161 (1938).

3. A. W. McCullough and E. L. Wilber, "A defect in the endocardial cushion development . . . cardiac anomaly," *Am. J. Path. 20,* 321–328 (1944).

4. F. Davies and M. A. MacConaill, "Cor biloculare, with a note on the development of the pulmonary veins," *J. Anat. 71,* 437–446 (1937).

5. J. E. Edwards, J. W. DuShane, D. W. Alcott, and H. H. Burchell, "Thoracic venous anomalies, III, IV," *Arch. Path. 51,* 446–460 (1951).

6. E. Loeffler, "Unusual malformations of the left atrium; pulmonary sinus," *Arch. Path. 48,* 371–376 (1949).

7. P. N. B. Odgers, "Development of the atrio-ventricular valves in man," *J. Anat. 73,* 643–657 (1939).

8. C. Ferencz, A. L. Johnson, and F. W. Wigglesworth, "Congenital mitral stenosis," *Circulation 9,* 161–179 (1954).

9. D. E. Harken, L. Dexter, L. B. Ellis, R. E. Farrano, and J. F. Dickson, III, "Surgery of mitral stenosis, III," *Ann. Surg. 134,* 722–741 (1951).

10. J. L. Bremer, "An interpretation of the development of the heart," *Am. J. Anat. 42,* 307–367 (1928).

11. T. C. Kramer, "The partitioning of the truncus and conus," *Am. J. Anat. 71,* 343–370 (1942).

12. R. E. Gross, "Surgical closure of an aortic septal defect," *Circulation 6,* 858–863 (1952).

13. R. T. Grant, "Development of the cardiac coronary vessels in the rabbit," *Heart 13,* 261–271.

REFERENCES

14. J. T. Wearn, S. R. Mettier, T. G. Klumpp, and L. J. Zschiesche, "Nature of vascular communications between the coronary arteries and the chambers of the heart," *Am. Heart J. 9*, 143–164 (1933).

15. A. Vineberg, D. D. Munro, H. Cohen, and W. Buller, "Internal mammary artery implantation in the treatment of coronary artery insufficiency," *J. Thoracic Surg. 29*, 1–36 (1955).

16. J. A. Key, F. G. Kergin, Y. Martineau, and R. G. Leekey, "A method of supplementing the coronary circulation by a jejunal pedicle graft," *J. Thoracic Surg. 28*, 320–330 (1954).

17. P. N. B. Odgers, "Development of the pars membranacea septi in the human heart," *J. Anat. 72*, 247–259 (1938).

18. S. Sato, "Ueber die Entwickelung der Atrioventricular-Klappen und der Pars membranacea . . . ," *Anat. Hefte 50*, 193–250 (1914).

19. R. W. Collett and J. E. Edwards, "Persistent truncus arteriosus: classification according to anatomical types," *S. Clin. North America 29*, 1245–1270 (1949).

20. J. E. Edwards, T. J. Dry, R. L. Parker, H. B. Burchell, E. H. Wood, and A. H. Bulbulian, *An atlas of congenital anomalies of the heart and great vessels* (Charles C Thomas, Springfield, Illinois, 1953).

21. S. Gibson, H. White, F. Johnson, and W. J. Potts, "Congenital pulmonary stenosis with intact ventricular septum," *Am. J. Dis. Child. 87*, 26–39 (1954).

22. R. F. Shaner, "Malformation of the atrio-ventricular cushions . . . relation to defects of the conus and truncus arteriosus," *Am. J. Anat. 84*, 431–455 (1949).

23. P. Gross, "Concept of fetal endocarditis," *Arch. Path. 31*, 163–177 (1941).

Chapter 10. Heart, III. Transposition of the Great Vessels

1. J. S. Harris and S. Farber, "Transposition of the great cardiac vessels—phylogenetic theory of Spitzer," *Arch. Path. 28*, 427–502 (1939).

2. E. Pernkopf and W. Wirtinger, "Die Transposition der Hertzostien," *Ztschr. f. Anat. u. Entwcklngsges. 100*, 563–734 (1933).

3. F. T. Lewis and M. Abbott, "Reversed twisting of the human heart," *Anat. Rec. 9*, 103–105 (1915).

4. T. Walmsley, "Transposition of the ventricles and the arterial stems," *J. Anat. 65*, 528–540 (1931).

5. R. F. Shaner, "Complete and corrected transposition of the aorta, pulmonary artery and ventricles in pig embryos, and a case of corrected transposition in a child," *Am. J. Anat. 88*, 35–62 (1951).

6. J. L. Bremer, "Transposition of the aorta and the pulmonary artery," *Arch. Path. 34*, 1016–1030 (1942).

7. B. I. Ivermark, "Implications of agenesis of the spleen on the pathogenesis of cono-truncus anomalies in childhood," *Acta paediat. 44*, supplement no. 104 (1955).

Chapter 11. Development of the Aortic Arches

1. E. D. Congdon, "Transformation of the aortic arch system . . . human embryo," *Carnegie Contrib. Embryol. 14*, 47–110 (1922).

2. G. J. Noback and I. Rehman, "The ductus arteriosus in the human fetus and newborn infant," *Anat. Rec. 81*, 505–527 (1941).

3. J. D. Boyd, "The nerve supply of the mammalian ductus arteriosus," *J. Anat. 75*, 457–468 (1941).

4. J. P. Schaeffer, "The behavior of elastic tissue in the post-fetal occlusion and obliteration of the ductus arteriosus (Botelli) in sus scrofa," *J. Exper. Med. 19*, 129–142 (1914).

5. E. Holman, F. Gerbode, and A. Purdy, "The patent ductus," *J. Thoracic Surg. 25*, 111–142 (1953).

6. R. E. Gross, "Complete division for the patent ductus arteriosus," *J. Thoracic Surg. 16*, 314–327 (1947).

7. C. F. De Garis, I. H. Black, and E. A. Riemenschneider, "Patterns of the aortic arch in American white and negro stocks," *J. Anat. 67*, 599–619 (1933).

8. J. J. McDonald and B. J. Anson. "Variations in the origin of arteries derived from the aortic arch . . . ," *Am. J. Phys. Anthropol. 27*, 91–108 (1940).

9. G. Holzapfel, "Ursprung and Verlauf der Arteria subclavia dextra," *Anat. Hefte 12*, 369–521 (1889).

10. A. Banchi, "Il V arco aortico branchiale . . . ," *Arch. ital. di anat. e di embriol. 6*, 389–427 (1907).

11. J. G. Wilson and J. Warkany, "Aortic arch and cardiac anomalies . . . vitamin A deficient rats," *Am. J. Anat. 85*, 113–155 (1949).

12. C. D. C. Baird, M. M. Nelson, I. W. Monte, and H. M. Evans, "Congenital cardiovascular anomalies . . . pteroylglutamic acid deficiency . . . ," *Circulation Rev. 2(b)*, 544–564 (1945).

13. E. B. D. Neuhauser, "Roentgen diagnosis of double aortic arch . . . ," *Am. J. Roentgenol. 56*, 1–12 (1946).

14. R. E. Gross and P. F. Ware, "Surgical significance of aortic arch anomalies," *Surg., Gynec. & Obst. 83*, 435–448 (1946).

15. L. M. Bonnet, "Stenose congenitale de l'aorte," *Rev. de méd., Paris 23*, 255, 355, 419, 481 (1903).

16. J. L. Bremer, "Coarctation of the aorta and the aortic isthmuses," *Arch. Pathol. 45*, 425–434 (1948).

INDEX

INDEX

INDEX